# THE LANGUAGE OF LOGIC

# THE LANGUAGE OF LOGIC / A Programed Text

**MORTON L. SCHAGRIN**

*Denison University*

**RANDOM HOUSE /** NEW YORK

# Acknowledgment

The primary debt any programer has is to the long-suffering students who tested the early versions. To them I again extend my gratitude for their assistance. Thanks are also due to the many colleagues, fellow programers, and reviewers, whose helpful suggestions have guided me in this work. This work could not have been done without the assistance and cooperation of the Programed Instruction Project of the Great Lakes Colleges Association.

This program was developed in part pursuant to a contract with the United States Office of Education, Department of Health, Education, and Welfare.

# Foreword

The symbolism of modern logic is being used more and more frequently in such diverse fields as mathematics, philosophy, psychology, economics, and others. In order to follow the discussion and arguments that employ this symbolism, students have either taken a formal course in modern logic or else have struggled through a textbook on the subject. The present book was designed to teach the symbolism of modern logic without becoming too deeply involved in the logical questions and proof techniques which comprise the major part of a course or normal textbook.

Specifically, the major goal of this book is to train the reader to recognize when a symbolic formula symbolizes an English sentence, and conversely when an English sentence interprets a symbolic formula.

Part I deals with the sentential calculus (SC) where sentences are treated as wholes and are not analyzed into smaller units that are not themselves sentences, such as subjects and predicates. Here one will learn the symbols for the common connectives such as 'and' and 'or'; how these connectives actually connect sentences; and the use of truth tables to determine logical equivalences.

Part II goes on to consider the predicate calculus with identity (PCI). Here one will learn the symbols for quantification; some standard forms of symbolization for common types of quantified sentences; and two simple techniques for determining logical equivalences and contradictions.

Behavioral Objectives for Part I can be found on page 1, and for Part II on page 103.

This book, then, is designed to give anyone of college ability sufficient familiarity with the symbolism of modern logic so that he may understand what is asserted by most authors using this symbolism. In my own course in the philosophy of science, for example, many of the reading assignments and much of the class discussion utilizes this symbolism. My students, in general, have not studied modern logic, and so must learn this symbolism. In the past I have had to take class time to present this material. Now, the present text teaches my students what they need to know, and we can begin right away with the substantive problems of the course.

Although the present text was not designed to supplement a course in modern symbolic logic, it would be of assistance to those students in such a course who have difficulty in symbolizing or interpreting. Anyone who uses this book as a supplement to a course in logic would do well to work through Part I only. Later when the course takes up the predicate calculus (first order functional calculus), he can try his hand at Part II.

The median time for working Part I is about 2 hours; for Part II, about 4 hours.

Finally, the symbolism dealt with in this book derives from Russell and Whitehead's *Principia Mathematica*. The so-called Polish notation is not used at all, nor are any modal symbols used.

## Apology to Logicians

Although the use-mention distinction has been observed in this program, no attempt has been made to call the reader's attention to it. To teach this distinction properly, and at the very beginning, would have increased the length of the program unduly. Besides, for many *applications* of the symbolism, the distinction is not critical. This program was not designed to be a rigorous introduction to logical theory. Thus if it is used in conjunction with a course in logic or semantics, some classroom time will have to be spent teaching the use-mention distinction.

# Instructions to the Reader

You are about to learn some skills. Merely reading about what to do will not make you skillful—try telling someone how to tie a bow knot. Therefore, you should be prepared to do something in order to learn.

Each frame of this program will present some material for you to think about. You will then be asked to perform some task such as: circle a word, pick an answer, fill in a blank, match some items, etc. Then either of two things will happen:

(1) The correct answer will be written below the place you performed the task and you will continue through the frame, or else the correct answer will appear at the bottom of the frame and you will be directed to turn to some other frame.    OR,

(2) After performing your task, you will be directed to turn to a new frame where you will find the correct answer. Frame numbers are the large numbers at the top of the page.

Whenever you have answered incorrectly, you should examine the correct answer carefully to see why you were wrong. In most cases the discussion following the correct answer will explain why it is the correct one. You may continue the program even if you are not *perfectly* clear why you were wrong (or right). BUT, when the directions sending you appear in a SHADED BOX (e.g., Turn to frame 31 ), you should not continue unless you understand why the correct answer is correct. You may even have to go back over the preceding section before you feel you fully understand the answer.

In order to help you avoid glancing at the answers, ANSWER SHIELDS are provided at various points in the program. These shields should be torn out of the book when you come to them. They can also be used for scratchwork and calculations, and some of them have useful summary notes printed on them. TEAR OUT pages are good resting places when you get tired.

A Self Examination with which you can test your mastery of the material appears at the end of the book.

# PART I   THE SENTENTIAL CALCULUS (SC)

## Objectives

Upon completion you should be able to:

(1) Select from a list of symbols those symbols corresponding to the five most common logical sentence connectives.
(2) Construct truth tables for each of these common sentence connectives.
(3) Select the symbolic formula of SC that correctly symbolizes a given compound English sentence of moderate complexity.
(4) Select an English sentence that correctly interprets a given formula of SC.
(5) Match basic formulae that are logically equivalent.

TEAR THIS SHEET OUT / You may use this sheet as your shield.
You may also do scratch work on it.

-------------------------------------- FOLD HERE --------------------------------------------

# 1

English sentences can be separated for logical purposes into those that are *simple* (or atomic) and those that are *compound* (or molecular).

SIMPLE SENTENCES:

    a. Small grey doves do coo at lonesome lovers.

    b. The corn is quite tall.

COMPOUND SENTENCES:

    a. Dogs lope while horses gallop.

    b. If the balance of terror persists, then the rate of cigarette smoking increases.

Roughly speaking, compound sentences are composed of two or more shorter simple sentences. CIRCLE the compound sentences in this list:

1. The quick brown fox jumped over the lazy dogs.

2. Roses are red and violets are blue.

3. Now is the time for all good men to come to the aid of the party.

4. Fat burns but water doesn't (burn).

5. He who never speaks never errs.

6. If a man never errs, then the Devil isn't happy.

7. Simple sentences standing alone are easy to detect; nevertheless it is often difficult to analyze a compound sentence into its component simple parts.

8. Seldom have so many owed so much to so few.

---

2. Roses are red and violets are blue.
4. Fat burns but water doesn't.
6. If a man never errs, then the Devil isn't happy.
7. Simple sentences standing alone are easy to detect; nevertheless it is often difficult to analyze a compound sentence into its component simple parts.

If you have missed any of these, turn to frame 3.

If you are correct on all of these, turn to frame 4.

5

# 2

You have not followed directions. This program cannot succeed in teaching you the language of logic until you understand the language of English.

Return to frame 1 and FOLLOW THE DIRECTIONS.

# 3

You missed one or more compound sentences.

Perhaps you should concentrate on identifying simple sentences. Simple sentences have no shorter sentences contained within them.

Example: DOGS BARK.

Now modifiers are irrelevant to the logical simplicity of a sentence.

Example: Small, shorthaired black dogs often bark fiercely.

This is still a simple sentence: Some thing (the subject) does something (the predicate).

Were we to compound **Dogs bark** with another simple sentence, we might obtain something like:

If *dogs bark,* then *cats purr.*

Circle the compound sentences below:

1. That doctor is a fraud or this druggist is a charlatan.

2. That child kicked this child in the stomach.

3. Aversive reinforcement is rewarding to a masochist.

4. I will not run if I am nominated, and I shall not serve if I am elected.

---

1. That doctor is a fraud or this druggist is a charlatan.
4. I will not run if I am nominated, and I shall not serve if I am elected.

If you are incorrect, go to frame 12.

If you are correct, go to frame 4.

# 4

Underline just the simple sentences in the following list which contains all the compound sentences from frame 1. Do not underline the connecting words.

Example: If <u>ducks bark</u>, then <u>cats quack</u> and <u>dogs purr</u>.

1. <u>Simple sentences standing alone are easy to detect</u>; nevertheless <u>it is often difficult to analyze a compound sentence into its component simple parts.</u>

2. <u>Roses are red</u> and <u>violets are blue.</u>

3. <u>Fat burns</u> but <u>water doesn't (burn).</u>

4. If <u>a man never errs</u>, then the <u>Devil isn't happy.</u>

Go to frame 5.

# 5

You probably have

1. Simple sentences standing alone are easy to detect; nevertheless <u>it is often difficult to analyze a compound sentence into its component simple parts</u>.
2. <u>Roses are red</u> and <u>violets are blue</u>.
3. <u>Fat burns</u> but <u>water doesn't</u>.
4. If <u>a man never errs</u>, then <u>the Devil isn't happy</u>.

Let's look more closely at the sentence:

The Devil isn't happy.

In a sense, this contains the shorter simple sentence:

The Devil is happy.

You may object to the metaphorical term 'contains'. If so, you may prefer to say that **The Devil isn't happy.** is logically related to **The Devil is happy.** Clearly, if one sentence is true, the other is false, and conversely. When sentences are so related, we shall say that one is the denial or <u>negation</u> of the other.

Write the simple sentences of which the following are denials:

1. This is not a simple sentence.

   *This is a simple sentence*

2. Violets aren't blue.

   *Violets are blue*

3. He cannot make it.

   *He can make it*

4. It is not the case that the moon is made of green cheese.

   *The moon is made of green cheese.*

---

1. This is a simple sentence.
2. Violets are blue.
3. He can make it.
4. The moon is made of green cheese.

Go to frame 6.

# 6

It will save space if, in any problem, we *abbreviate* the simple sentences by using capital letters. For example,

S̲  abbreviates **This is a simple s̲entence**.
B̲  abbreviates **Violets are b̲lue**.

M: He can m̲ake it.
G: The moon is made of g̲reen cheese.

We can now (partially) symbolize the *negations* of these simple sentences as:

not S            not M
not B            it is not the case that G

Indeed we shall go further and write a        ~        to the left of any sentence to symbolize its *denial*.

| ENGLISH SENTENCE | SYMBOLIC FORMULA |
|---|---|
| This is not a simple sentence | ~S |
| Violets aren't blue. | ~B |
| He cannot make it. | ~M |
| It is not the case that the moon is made of green cheese. | ~G |

(Fill in the above blank spaces.)

---

Violets aren't blue: ~B
He cannot make it: ~M

Next frame.

# 7

Using '~' complete the examples.

1. Fat burns but water does not.
   - F: Fat burns.
   - W: Water burns.

   F but ~W

2. It is not the case that both all redheads are communists and all redheads are capitalists.
   - C: All redheads are communists.
   - A: All redheads are capitalists.

   ~both C and A

3. Either Jones isn't guilty or I'll turn in my badge.
   - J: Jones is guilty.
   - B: I'll turn in my badge.

   Either ~J or B

   (Fill in.)

---

Either ~J or B

---

4. If dogs bark, then cats don't swim.
   - D: Dogs bark.
   - C: Cats swim.

   If D, then ~C

5. Although roses are red, violets aren't blue.
   - R: Roses are red.
   - B: Violets are blue.

   Althō R, ~B

---

Although R, ~B

---

6. It is not the case that if it rains then the day is ruined.
   - R: It rains.
   - D: The day is ruined.

   ~ If R then D

---

6. ~If R then D

If you were wrong on *either* 5 or 6, go to frame 8.

If both have been correct, go to frame 9.

# 8

You are having some trouble placing the negation sign in the right spot. The trick to this is to
1. find the sentence being denied
2. find its abbreviation, or symbolization if it is compound
3. write the symbolized negation in the larger sentence without changing any of the connective words.

For instance:

That *won't* work, *or else* I am a monkey's uncle.
W: That will work.
M: I am a monkey's uncle.

~W, or else M

*It is not the case that either* 2 is odd *or* 6 is prime.
O: 2 is odd.
P: 6 is prime.

~either O or P

(Here the entire sentence **either O or P** is denied.)

Let's try some more:

1. Airplanes frighten me *but* sailboats *don't*.
A: Airplanes frighten me.
S: Sailboats frighten me.

A but ~S

---

1. A but ~S

---

2. If you eat ice cream with pickles, then you will not sleep well tonight.
P: You eat ice cream with pickles.
S: You will sleep well tonight.

If P then ~S

---

2. If P then ~S

Go to frame 10.

# 9

One final example:

If sugar is not soluble, then neither is salt.
  S: Sugar is soluble.
  A: Salt is soluble.

If ~S then ~A

---

If ~S then ~A

Go to frame 11.

# 10

One final example:

If sugar is not soluble, then neither is salt.
  S: Sugar is soluble.
  A: Salt is soluble.

---

If ~S then ~A

If you are correct, go to frame 11.

If you are still incorrect, go to frame 12.

# 11

Different authors use different signs to symbolize *denial*. You should be familiar with some of the common variations. In addition to ~ you will find:  —  and  ￢

Of course, any one author will use just one of these. So the *negation* of **S** may be found in one of these ways:

$$\sim S \qquad\qquad -S \qquad\qquad \neg S$$

Write the denial of **Roses are red**. (abbreviated: R) in the three different ways indicated above.

~R

—R

￢R

Do not turn to next frame, go to frame 13.

# 12

You are here because you are having difficulties with fairly easy but basic material.

Put this book away for a while and do something else, or perhaps have a cup of coffee. Then come back and review the section where you are having trouble. If you still find that you do not understand the material, consult with your instructor, or someone who knows some logic.

# 13

Recall that ~**R** (or ¬**R** or −**R**) is a true sentence if **R** is false. Denial is the first truth functional compound we shall learn.

Another compound whose truth value (True or False) depends on the truth values of its components is the *conjunction* of two sentences. In English the word 'and' is often used *conjunctively*, although the word 'but' frequently conjoins two sentences.

Circle the word in the last sentence above that is being used to conjoin the two simple sentences there.

Although

Go to frame 14.

# 14

The English language has many devices to signalize conjunction; even punctuation marks can play this role. We shall use a dot between two symbolized sentences to construct their conjunction.

For instance, **Although roses are red, violets aren't blue.** which was abbreviated as **Although R, ~B** will henceforth be written  **(R ·~B)** ·

The dot is again not completely standard. You will occasionally find an author who uses      &      or      ∧      where we use      ·

Hence the sentence **Roses are red and violets are blue.** will be variously symbolized as:

(R · B)            (R ∧ B)                (R & B)

Circle those formulae that symbolize conjunctions. (Remember: Capital letters are abbreviations of complete simple sentences.)

1. (~A ϵ B)                 6. (¬L ∧ M)

2. (C &~~D)                 7. (~N +~O)

3. (E □ F)                  8. (−P · Q)

4. (G ∨ H)                  9. ((R · S) · T)

5. (J · K)                  10. (~U & V)

---

2. (C &~~D)            8. (−P · Q)
5. (J · K)             9. ((R · S) · T)
6. (¬L ∧ M)            10. (~U & V)

Go to frame 15.

# 15

These symbols are never mixed. An author will choose one of them and never use the others.

| CORRECT | INCORRECT |
|---|---|
| (~A · ~B) | (~A · — B) |
| ((C & D) & E) | ((C · D) & E) |
| ((¬¬A ∧ B) ∧ C) | ((¬~A ∧ B) · C) |
| ((F · G) · (H · J)) | ((F · G) ∧ (H · J) |

Write the technical names of the two sorts of compound sentences we have learned.

C o n j u n c t i o __N__

D e n i a __L__   or   N e g a _____ TION

Go to frame 16.

# 16

From the list below, select the symbols corresponding to the logical connections, and copy them in the indicated spaces. Try not to check back on this one.

☆　~　&　→　∨　·　¬　≡　∧　□　△　—　+

Conjunction _&_ · _∧_

Denial or Negation _~ ¬ —_

---

Conjunction ∧ · &
Denial ~ ¬ —

Go to frame 17. But first check p. vii if you don't remember about shaded instructions.

20

# 17

We can go on to introduce more symbols, <u>or</u> we can stop now. The latter *alternative* is not as defeatist as it may sound, and you can refer to any modern logic textbook to see how much can be done with only the concepts of denial and conjunction. However we will go on to take a look at some new symbols.

Underline the connective in the paragraph above før which we have *not* introduced a symbol.

Go to frame 18.

# 18

EITHER you found it easily OR you are not concentrating on the tasks in this program.

Fortunately there is only one symbol used by everyone for *alternation*, or as some call it, *disjunction*. The first sentence of this page is a disjunction and is symbolized like this:

(E ∨ ~C)
    E: You found it easily.
    C: You are concentrating on the tasks in this program.

Now you try to symbolize a *disjunction*:

This bridge is safe, or Jones is a poor engineer.
    B: This bridge is safe.
    J: Jones is a poor engineer.

$(\underline{B \vee J})$
(Answer.)

Parenthesis!

---

(B ∨ J)

Did you forget parentheses? If so, put them in and everyone go to frame 19.

# 19

(**B** ∨ **J**) asserts that one of two things is the case. Could we maintain the truth of the compound if both alternatives were True? That is, suppose the bridge *is* safe, and still Jones is a poor engineer, is (**B** ∨ **J**) True or False?

Lawyers use the term 'and/or' to express the condition that either of two sentences *or possibly both* are True. We shall always use '∨' in the sense of the lawyers' 'and/or'. Hence (**B** ∨ **J**) *is a False compound only when* **B** *and* **J** *are* BOTH *False sentences.*

Now, suppose **A** is some True sentence (it doesn't matter which), and **B** is some False sentence. What is the truth value of (**A** ∨ **B**)?

True/False _____

True, go to frame 21.

False, go to frame 20.

23

# 20

You're not concentrating. Since at least one *disjunct* is True, the whole disjunction is True.

Return to frame 19 and read the material again. Then choose the correct answer.

# 21

(**A** ∨ **B**) is True since not both disjuncts are False.

Let's try some more. Determine if the indicated compound is True or False, given the truth values of the component sentences.

1. (C ∨ D)
   where **C** is False
   and **D** is True                                        *true*

2. (E ∨ F)
   where **E** is True
   and **F** is True                                        *true*

3. (G ∨ H)
   where **G** is False
   and **H** is False                                       *false*

4. (J ∨ ~K)
   where **J** is False
   and **K** is False                                       *true*

---

Only (**G** ∨ **H**) is False. In the last example, **K** is False, therefore its negation ~**K** is True. Thus, not both disjuncts are False and the whole disjunction is True.

If you missed 1, 2, or 3, return to frame 19 and study what is said there. Then continue reworking the program.

If you missed 4, go to frame 22.

If you were completely right, go to frame 23.

# 22

You did not realize that (**J** ∨ ~**K**) is True when **J** is False and **K** is False.

We are disjoining, or alternating, **J** and ~**K**. In order to determine the truth value of the disjunction, we must first determine the truth value of the disjuncts. The truth value of **J** is given to us as False. But the truth value of ~**K**, the other disjunct, must be calculated from the truth value of **K**. Since **K** is False, ~**K** is True. Hence we have a disjunction of a False sentence, **J**, and a True one, ~**K**.

A disjunction is False only when *both* disjuncts are False.

Go to frame 23.

# 23

Circle one choice:

1. A negation of a True sentence is a (True/False) sentence.

2. A conjunction of two True sentences is a (True/False) sentence.

3. If one *conjunct* of a conjunction is a False sentence, the entire conjunction is a (True/False) sentence.

---

1. False
2. True
3. False

---

4. Circle in the list below the symbols often used for negation:

∧      ~      ☆      □      ¬      &

---

4. ~ ¬

---

5. Write out another common symbol for negation      _____

---

5. —

---

6. Circle in the list below the symbols often used for conjunction:

☆    ~    ∧    □    ¬    ∨    ↓    &    @        ¢

---

6. ∧ & ·

Next frame.

# 24

Have we the capability of symbolizing an *exclusive alternation*? Suppose we want to symbolize:

You may have some candy or you may have some ice cream, *but not both*.

Replacing the simple sentences by obvious abbreviations, we obtain:

C or R but not both

We should expand this compound to the more explicit one:

C or R but not both C and R

Circle the correct symbolizations of this:

No mixing

1. ((C ∧ R) &~C) & R
2. (C ∨ R) &~(C · R)
3. (C ∨ R) ·¬(C · R)

4. (C ∨ R) &−(C & R)
5. (C · R) ·~(C ∨ R)
6. ((C ∨ R) ·~C) · R

7. (C ∨ R) ∧~(C ∧ R)

Note: Outermost parentheses will be omitted if no ambiguity results. Strictly speaking, there should be an additional pair of parentheses enclosing each of the above formulae.

NB

---

3. (C ∨ R)·¬(C · R)      4. (C ∨ R) &−(C & R)      7. (C ∨ R) ∧~(C ∧ R)
2. *fails* because it mixes '&' and '·'.

Disregard 2. If you are correct on all the others, turn to frame 26.

If you missed any besides 2, turn to frame 25.

# 25

**C or R but not both C and R** should be broken up piece by piece. The major break in this sentence occurs at 'but' which, in this context, signals a conjunction. Hence we have a conjunction of two sentences:

> **C or R** and **not both C and R**
> **C or R** can be symbolized only one way: (C ∨ R)

The second conjunct, **not both C and R**, is the negation of **both C and R**: not **both C and R**. Choosing some representative negation and conjunction symbols, we have for instance: ¬(C ∧ R)

Now we must conjoin **(C ∨ R)** with ¬**(C ∧ R)**. Since we have already chosen '∧' for conjunction, we get **(C ∨ R) ∧ ¬(C ∧ R)**

The other correct choices are obtained from the above by changing the symbols throughout for denial and conjunction.

Go to frame 26.

# 26

The final two connectives we shall study are perhaps the most important from the point of view of deduction techniques. We have already met with examples of *conditional* sentences: they have the form

> If . . ., then _____.

An example of a *biconditional* sentence is:

> You will pass the course *if and only if* you pass the final examination.

This means:

> If you pass the final examination, then you will pass the course, and if you do not pass the final examination, then you will not pass the course.

There are two accepted ways of symbolizing the *conditional* and the *biconditional.*

| CONDITIONAL | BICONDITIONAL |
|---|---|
| $\supset$ | $\equiv$ |
| $\rightarrow$ | $\leftrightarrow$ |

Circle the symbolic formula that symbolizes the given English sentence.

1. *If* it rains, *then* we do *not* go on the picnic *and* we stay home.

    R: It rains.
    P: We go on the picnic.
    S: We stay home.

    $\sim(R \supset P)\ \&\ S$

    $\boxed{R \supset (\sim P \cdot S)}$

    $R \supset (\neg P \lor S)$

    $(R \supset - P) \cdot S$

2. *If* the wind is *not* too strong *and* it is *not* raining, we can have the race.

    W: The wind is too strong.
    R: It is raining.
    H: We can have the race.

    $(\sim W\ \&\sim R)\ \&\ H$

    $\sim W \rightarrow \sim(R \cdot H)$

    $\sim W \supset (\sim R \supset H)$

    $\boxed{(\sim W \cdot \sim R) \rightarrow H}$

*continued*

3. We are staying home, and furthermore, if it is sunny, then we shall miss the swim.

    H: We are staying home.

    S: It is sunny.

    M: We shall miss the swim.

$(H \supset S) \mathrel{\&} M$

$H \supset (S \supset M)$

$(H \cdot S) \rightarrow M$

$\boxed{H \cdot (S \rightarrow M)}$

---

3. $H \cdot (S \rightarrow M)$

---

4. If Harrison wins the presidency, or if the socialist party gains a majority, the country is doomed.

    H: Harrison wins the presidency.

    S: The socialist party gains a majority.

    C: The country is doomed.

$H \supset (S \lor C)$

$\boxed{(H \lor S) \supset C}$

$H \lor \supset (S \supset C)$

$(H \cdot S) \rightarrow C$

---

4. $(H \lor S) \supset C$

The formula **H ∨ ⊃ (S ⊃ C)** is not well-formed and does not symbolize *any* sentence at all.

If either of these is incorrect, go to frame 27.

If they are both correct, go to frame 28.

# 27

You are having trouble identifying the 'if' clause, and the 'then' clause. These clauses may be compound, or the conditional 'If . . ., then _____' sentence may be compounded with something else.

Try using parentheses on the English sentence.

1. (If you are right then I apologize), but (I think you are wrong.)
      R                  A                    W

   $(R \rightarrow A) \cdot W$

2. If c = 7 then (either a = 3 or b = 5).
     C                       A     B

   $C \supset (A \lor B)$

Circle the correct choice in 3.

3. If Jones is present and Smith is absent, something important is going on.
    J: Jones is present.
    S: Smith is absent.
    I: Something important is going on.

                                      $J \rightarrow (S \cdot I)$

                                  $(J \& S) \supset I$

                                  $(J \supset S) \supset I$

                                  $(J \& S) \& I$

---

3. $(J \& S) \supset I$

If you are correct, return to frame 26 and rework the problems, before you continue the program.

If you are incorrect, go to frame 12.

# 28

Great care must be taken to determine which sentence is the *ante-cedent*, and which the *consequent* of a conditional compound.

Example:  You will find him if you turn right at the corner.
                    H                         R

      is symbolized:     (R ⊃ H)

Furthermore, the phrase 'only if' is highly deceptive.

Example:  You may enter only if you have a ticket.

      This may be rephrased which way? Underline one.

      1. If you have a ticket then you may enter.

      2. If you enter then you have a ticket.

Wrong

Choice 1, go to frame 29.

Choice 2, go to frame 30.

33

# 29

The sentence **You may enter *only if* you have a ticket.** means that your having a ticket is *necessary* for you to enter, but it may not be sufficient. After all, even if you have your ticket, the theater may be filled, you may not be properly dressed, you could be drunk, etc. Therefore, **If you enter then (at least) you have a ticket.** is closer in meaning to our original sentence.

Go on to the next frame.

34

# 30

You said **You may enter only if you have a ticket** may be rephrased **If you enter then you have a ticket.** Correct; you realized that even if you have a ticket, you still might not enter (e.g., the theater might be filled).

Happily these problems do not arise with the biconditional ($\equiv$, $\leftrightarrow$). There is no need to distinguish the left hand sentence from the right hand one, as we had to distinguish antecedent from consequent in a conditional.

Symbolize:

> *If and only if* the time is ripe, will the revolution succeed.
> T: The time is ripe.
> R: The revolution will succeed.

$$T \equiv R$$
(Answer.)

---

Any of these four are correct:
(T $\equiv$ R)                    (T $\leftrightarrow$ R)
(R $\equiv$ T)                    (R $\leftrightarrow$ T)

Go on to frame 31.

# 31

From the list below, select the symbols corresponding to the logical connections and copy them in the indicated spaces.

≢ & ☆ ⊬ ⊬ □ ⊬ ⊬ † / △ ⊅ ⋏ ⋏ ∘ ⊬

Denial _~_ _–_ _¬_ _⌐_

Conditional _→_ _⊃_ _⊬_

Conjunction _∧_ _·_ _&_ _⊬_

Biconditional _≡_ _↔_ _⊬_

Disjunction _∨_ _⊬_

---

Denial ~ ¬ –
Conditional ⊃ →
Conjunction & · ∧
Biconditional ≡ ↔
Disjunction ∨

Go to page 37.

36

TEAR THIS SHEET OUT  /  You may use this sheet as your new shield and as a reference sheet. You may also do scratch work on it.

Denial  ∼  ¬  —

Conjunction  ∧  &  ·

Disjunction  ∨

Conditional  →  ⊃

Biconditional  ↔  ≡

-------------------------------------- FOLD HERE --------------------------------------

37

# 32

We shall now learn how the truth value of a compound is a *function* of the truth values of its components. Since we wish to be quite general about this, we shall not use *actual* sentences which are in fact True or False but rather *variables* such as: p, q, r, s.

Using these lower case letters (and others if we need them) we can avoid such tedious and turgid remarks as:

The denial of any sentence is symbolized by a tilde, '~', written immediately to the left of the symbolization of that sentence.

Using a variable, we say instead: The denial of any sentence p is ~p. *Instances* of this usage are:

| PARTICULAR SENTENCES | THEIR DENIALS |
|---|---|
| B | ~B |
| (C ∨ D) | ~(C ∨ D) |
| ((E ⊃ F) ≡ G) | ~((E ⊃ F) ≡ G) |
| ~H | ~~H |

Letting 'T' and 'F' abbreviate 'True' and 'False' respectively, we can show in tabular form how the truth value of a denial is a function of the truth value of the sentence denied:

| p | ~p |
|---|---|
| T | F |
| F | T |

This *truth table* shows that for *any* sentence p,
    when p is T, ~p is _____*F*_____
    when p is F, ~p is _____*T*_____
(Fill in blanks.)

---

p is T, ~p is F
p is F, ~p is T

Go to frame 33.

# 33

We have learned that a disjunction, (p ∨ q), is False only when both disjuncts are False, and the compound is True in any other case. For *any* two *arbitrary* sentences p and q, we can list all possible truth value combinations of them:

| | p | q | |
|---|---|---|---|
| Case 1. both True | T | T | |
| Case 2. p True; q False | T | F | |
| Case 3. p False; q True | F | T | |
| Case 4. both False | F | F | |

Only in case 4 is the disjunction of these two sentences False. We write 'F' for that case:

| p | q | (p ∨ q) |
|---|---|---|
| T | T | |
| T | F | |
| F | T | |
| F | F | F |

Now construct the complete truth table for (p ∨ q).

| p | q | (p ∨ q) |
|---|---|---|
| T | T | T |
| T | F | T |
| F | T | T |
| F | F | F |

Go to next frame.

# 34

A disjunction is False only when both disjuncts are False; in all other cases the disjunction is True.

| p | q | (p ∨ q) |
|---|---|---------|
| T | T | T |
| T | F | T |
| F | T | T |
| F | F | F |

What about conjunctions? When I assert p and q conjointly, I intend that both p and q are the case. If either of, or both, p and q are False, my conjoint assertion of them, (p and q), is likewise False.

Complete the truth table for conjunction.

|       | p | q | (p & q) |
|-------|---|---|---------|
| Row 1 | T | T | T |
| Row 2 | T | F | F. |
| Row 3 | F | T | F |
| Row 4 | F | F | F |

Go to next frame.

# 35

Compare the truth table for *conjunction* with that for *disjunction*; note the symmetry.

| p | q | (p · q) | (p ∨ q) |
|---|---|---------|---------|
| T | T | T | T |
| T | F | F | T |
| F | T | F | T |
| F | F | F | F |

This symmetry is important both for remembering the significance of the concepts of conjunction and disjunction, and for analyzing more complicated compound sentences.

Remember, p and q were understood to be *any arbitrary* sentences, either simple or compound. We can analyze complicated compound sentences by means of truth tables and tell under what conditions these complicated sentences *would be* True or False.

| p | ~p | ~~p | ~~~p | ~~~~p |
|---|----|-----|------|-------|
| T | F | T | F | T |
| F | T | F | T | F |

From this table we see that ~~~~p is F when p is F. Complete the table and determine when ~~p is F and when ~~~p is T.

If you have:

Turn to:

1.  ~~p is F, when p is T, and
    ~~~p is T, when p is F                     frame 36.

2.  ~~p is F, when p is F, and
    ~~~p is T, when p is T                     frame 37.

3.  ~~p is F, when p is F, and
    ~~~p is T, when p is F                     frame 38.

4.  ~~p is F, when p is T, and
    ~~~p is T, when p is T                     frame 39.

42

# 36

You have made a mistake. You can go back and try again, or go to frame 37 for a little explanation of *why* you have erred.

# 37

You've made a mistake somewhere, or perhaps you are confused about the *use* of truth tables. A little common sense reasoning should have warned you about your error. After all, ~~~p is the denial of ~~p. Therefore, ~~~p is True and ~~p is False for some *one* truth value of p, either T or F. So the correct answer is either 3 or 4.

Go back to frame 35 and work out the truth table again. Then select 3 or 4.

But if you want more help, go to frame 39.

44

# 38

Choice 3 is correct. From the truth table we see that ~~p is F in the bottom row, which is when p (the far left column) is F. Similarly for ~~~p.

In order to find the conditions under which a given compound sentence would be True or False, we first must determine the *logical form* of the sentence. This is easily done by *replacing the actual component simple sentences by variables.*

Complete the following examples. NOTE, however, that the actual sentences abbreviated by the capital letters are not important.

1. ~~(A ·~B)           ~~(p ·~q)

2. E ⊃ (M ∨¬(E & G))     p ⊃ (q ∨¬(p & r))
     (Notice that *each* occurrence of 'E' is replaced by 'p'.)

3. K ∧ (L ∧ S)          p ∧ (q ∧ r)

4. H ≡ (J ⊃ L)          p ≡ (q ⊃ R)

5. ~(~A ∨~B)            ~(~p ∨~B)

6. C &−D               p &−q

7. K ≡ (K ≡ K)          p ≡ (p ≡ p)

_____

4. p ≡ (q ⊃ r)              6. p &−q
5. ~(~p ∨~q)               7. p ≡ (p ≡ p)

If you have any wrong, you did not understand the directions.
Leaving the parentheses and connective symbols untouched, simply replace
each capital letter by a variable. If a capital letter occurs more than
once, use the same variable at each occurrence. Go on to frame 40.

# 39

Something's wrong. Check this truth table against yours in frame 35.

| p | ~p | ~~p | ~~~p | ~~~~p |
|---|----|-----|------|-------|
| T | F  | T   | F    | T     |
| F | T  | F   | T    | F     |

The top row alternates T and F; the bottom row alternates F and T.

Looking at the top of the columns, we see that each formula is followed on the *right* by its denial. Thus the truth value is reversed at each step to the right.

We see then that ~~p is F (bottom row) when, reading to the left, ~p is T and p is F. So when *any arbitrary* sentence p is F, its *double negation*, ~~p, is also F.

Similarly, ~~~p is T (still bottom row) when ~~p is F, hence a triple negation is T, when the original sentence is F.

Study the construction of the truth table at the top of this page and then turn back to frame 38.

# 40

We now can determine by truth tables when any compound sentence of a given logical form is True or when it is False. *We simply construct the sentence from its progressively more complex parts.*

Take, for example:
> We will not go to the *movies* and we will not go to the party.

Symbolized: (~M ·~G)
Its logical form is: (~p ·~q)

We observe that we are *conjoining* ~p and ~q, hence

| | p | q | ~p | ~q | (~p ·~q) |
|---|---|---|---|---|---|
| Row 1 | T | T | F | F | F |
| Row 2 | T | F | F | T | F |
| Row 3 | F | T | T | F | F |
| Row 4 | F | F | T | T | T |

Since a conjunction is True only when both conjuncts are True, you should be able to complete the above table. Do so.

| p | q | ~p ·~q |
|---|---|---|
| T | T | F |
| T | F | F |
| F | T | F |
| F | F | T |

If you are not sure what you are doing, or have made a mistake in the above table, turn to frame 41. Otherwise go to frame 42.

47

# 41

We are working with $\sim$**M** $\cdot\sim$**G**. We want to know the conditions under which such a sentence is True (or False). But this sentence is clearly the conjunction of two shorter sentences, and we know the truth conditions for a conjunction: *A conjunction is True only when both conjuncts are True.*

Now our problem is to determine under what conditions both conjuncts are simultaneously True. The conjuncts here are $\sim$**M** and $\sim$**G**. Each of these is True, when the simple sentences **M** and **G** are False. And *only then.*

All this is summarized neatly in our truth table, where for two arbitrary *simple* sentences, we first determine the truth values of their negations ($\sim$p and $\sim$q) and then, following the arrows, the truth values (for all possible cases) of the conjunction of these negations, ($\sim$p $\cdot\sim$q).

We'll get more practice with this in a moment. Meanwhile, turn to frame 42.

# 42

Fill in the following truth tables:

| p | ~p |
|---|---|
| T | F |
| F | T |

| p | q | (p & q) |
|---|---|---|
| T | T | T |
| T | F | F |
| F | T | F |
| F | F | F |

| p | q | (p ∨ q) |
|---|---|---|
| T | T | T |
| T | F | T |
| F | T | T |
| F | F | F |

The answers are in the next frame.

# 43

1. If a sentence is True, its *negation* is False, and if a sentence is False, its negation is True.

| p | ~p |
|---|---|
| T | F |
| F | T |

2. A *conjunction* is True if both components (conjuncts) are True, otherwise it is False.

| p | q | (p · q) |
|---|---|---|
| T | T | T |
| T | F | F |
| F | T | F |
| F | F | F |

3. A *disjunction* or *alternation* is False if both components (disjuncts) are False, otherwise it is True.

| p | q | (p ∨ q) |
|---|---|---|
| T | T | T |
| T | F | T |
| F | T | T |
| F | F | F |

Turn to p. 51.

TEAR THIS SHEET OUT  /  You may use this sheet as your new shield and as a reference sheet. You may also do scratch work on it.

DO NOT MAKE NOTES.

Denial  ∼ ¬ −

Conjunction & ∧ ·                                    Conditional ⊃ →
Disjunction ∨                                        Biconditional ≡ ↔

| p | ~p |
|---|-----|
| T | F  |
| F | T  |

| p | q | (p · q) | (p ∨ q) |
|---|---|---------|---------|
| T | T | T       | T       |
| T | F | F       | T       |
| F | T | F       | T       |
| F | F | F       | F       |

------------------------------ FOLD HERE ------------------------------

51

# 44

When we assert a conditional such as:

> If the temperature exceeds 500° C, the sample will melt.

under what conditions are we willing to admit that our assertion is False? Under what conditions may we claim Truth for it?

Actually, for some conditionals, there is room for discussion as to what precisely is meant. Just as we took the "weakest" reading for 'or' so we will now take the weakest sense of an 'If . . ., then _____' sentence.

At *the very least*, when we say:

> (1) If the temperature exceeds 500° C, the sample will melt.

we mean to *deny* that:

> (2) The temperature exceeds 500° C and the sample does not melt.

Let:

T: The temperature exceeds 500° C.
S: The sample melts.

Now on the one hand we are asserting (1), (If T then S): $(T \supset S)$ and on the other hand *denying* (2), (T and not S): $(T \cdot \neg S)$

We shall let the truth table for any conditional $(p \supset q)$ be defined by the truth table for the *denial* of $(p \cdot \neg q)$. ←

|  | p | q | ¬q | p · ¬q | ¬ (p · ¬q) |
|---|---|---|---|---|---|
| Row 1 | T | T | F | F | T |
| Row 2 | T | F | T | T | F |
| Row 3 | F | T | F | F | T |
| Row 4 | F | F | T | F | T |

By our decision, $(p \rightarrow q)$ is False in one and only one case. For what truth values of p and q is $(p \rightarrow q)$ False?

Write in 'T' or 'F' as appropriate: p __T__; q __F__.

Go to next frame.

# 45

(p → q) is False only when p is T and q is F.

We have already expressed the intent of a *biconditional* without using the phrase 'if and only if' (sometimes written: iff). Recall that the sentence

> You will pass the course if and only if you pass the final examination.

whose logical form is: $(q \equiv p)$ was expressed by another sentence:

> If you pass the final examination, then you will pass the course, and if you do not pass the final examination, then you will not pass the course.

whose logical form is: $(p \supset q) \cdot (\sim p \supset \sim q)$

*Help!*

| p | q | p ⊃ q | ~p | ~q | ~p ⊃ ~q | (p ⊃ q) · (~p ⊃ ~q) |
|---|---|---|---|---|---|---|
| T | T | T | F | F | T | *T* ✓ |
| T | F | F. | F | T | T | *F* ✓ |
| F | T | T | T | F | F. | *F* ✓ |
| F | F | T | T | T | T | *T* ✓ |

conjunction of these two

Fill in the truth table. What are the truth conditions for a biconditional?

(p ↔ q) is True when _p ⊃ q is T ≠ ~p ⊃ ~Q_ _is True_

(p ↔ q) is False when _when p ⊃ q is true_ _& ~p ⊃ ~Q is false or when p ⊃ q is false & ~p ⊃ ~Q is true_

Go to next frame.

# 46

A biconditional is True if both the right and left components have the same truth value (i.e., True or False), and a biconditional is False if its major components differ in truth value.

| p | q | p ⊃ q | ~p | ~q | ~p ⊃ ~q | (p ⊃ q) · (~p ⊃ ~q) | p ≡ q |
|---|---|-------|----|----|---------|---------------------|-------|
| T | T | T | F | F | T | T | T |
| T | F | F | F | T | T | F | F |
| F | T | T | T | F | F | F | F |
| F | F | T | T | T | T | T | T |

Check this table with the one you filled out in the previous frame.

If there are any errors, go to frame 47.

If you are entirely correct, go to frame 48.

| p | q | p ⊃ q | ~p | ~q | ~p ⊃ ~q | (p ⊃ q) · (~p ⊃ ~q) |
|---|---|---|---|---|---|---|
| T | T | T | F | F | T | T |
| T | F | F | F | T | T | F |
| F | T | T | T | F | F | F |
| F | F | T | T | T | T | T |

1. The column under ~p exhibits the truth value of the negation of p. By reference to the column under p we can see how the truth value of ~p is a function of the truth value of p. Similarly for ~q. Fill in these two columns.

2. The column under (~p ⊃ ~q) exhibits the truth value of this *conditional*, and shows how the truth value is a function of the truth values of p and q. In constructing this column, we note when the antecedent, ~p, is T and the consequent, ~q, is F. That is the only time (~p ⊃ ~q) is F. This occurs in *row* 3. Fill in the column.

3. The column under (p ⊃ q) · (~p ⊃ ~q) exhibits the truth value of this *conjunction* as a function of the truth values p and q. In constructing this column we use the *concept of conjunction* whereby a conjunction is T only when both conjuncts [in this case, (p ⊃ q) and (~p ⊃ ~q)] are T. This occurs in rows 1 and 4. Fill in the last column.

Go to next frame.

# 48

Another way to rephrase a biconditional is preferred by some people. The biconditional

    p if and only if q

is often re-expressed as

    if p then q, and if q then p

symbolized:   (p ⊃ q) · (q ⊃ p)

To show that (p ≡ q) is *logically equivalent* to (p ⊃ q) · (q ⊃ p), we need show only that *their truth tables are identical.* That is, we show two sentences to be logically equivalent if we show that under the same conditions both are True or both are False.

| p | q | p ⊃ q | q ⊃ p | (p ⊃ q) & (q ⊃ p) | p ≡ q |
|---|---|---|---|---|---|
| T | T | *T* | *T* | *T* | T |
| T | F | *F* | *T* | *F* | F |
| F | T | *T* | *F* | *F* | F |
| F | F | *T* | *T* | *T* | T |

*Help!*

Fill in the above truth table taking care to distinguish the antecedent and consequent in (q ⊃ p).

| p | q | p ⊃ q | q ⊃ p | (p ⊃ q) & (q ⊃ p) | p ≡ q |
|---|---|---|---|---|---|
| T | T | T | T | T | T |
| T | F | F | T | F | F |
| F | T | T | F | F | F |
| F | F | T | T | T | T |

If correct, go to frame 50.

If you made any mistakes, correct them, and then go to frame 50.

# 49

You are not following instructions very carefully, are you?

Please do not skim through this program. You will learn from this program only if you do the tasks carefully and conscientiously, and read the directions when you have completed the tasks.

# 50

You should now be able to construct a truth table for the conditional and the biconditional without any further help.

| p | q | p ⊃ q | p ≡ q |
|---|---|-------|-------|
| T | T | T | T |
| T | F | T | F |
| F | T | T | F |
| F | F | T | T |

---

| p | q | p ⊃ q | p ≡ q |
|---|---|-------|-------|
| T | T | T | T |
| T | F | F | F |
| F | T | T | F |
| F | F | T | T |

If you are correct, go to frame 52.

If there are any errors, or if you are unsure of the concepts of the conditional and biconditional, turn to next frame.

# 51

The essential point of a conditional compound sentence is that it is *False only when the antecedent is True and the consequent is False.* In a truth table for the conditional (p ⊃ q), the role of the antecedent is played by p; for (q ⊃ p), the antecedent is q; and for (p ∨ q) ⊃ (r · s), the antecedent is (p ∨ q) and the consequent is (r · s).

So, if we were constructing a truth table for (p ∨ q) ⊃ (r · s), we would enter F in any row where (p ∨ q) was T and (r · s) was F. And if we were constructing a table for (~p ⊃ ~q), we would enter F in any row where ~p was T and ~q was F.

A biconditional is *T when both components have the same truth value.* Thus, (p ∨ q) ≡ (r · s) would have T placed in any row where either (p ∨ q) and (r · s) were T, or (p ∨ q) and (r · s) were F. For simply (p ≡ q), those rows where either p and q are T, or p and q are F, have a T in them.

|     | p | q | r | (q ∨ r) | p ⊃ (q ∨ r) | p · q | ~q | ~q · r | (p · q) ≡ (~q · r) |
|-----|---|---|---|---------|-------------|-------|----|--------|---------------------|
| 1.  | T | T | T |         |             |       |    |        |                     |
| 2.  | T | T | F |         |             |       |    |        |                     |
| 3.  | T | F | T |         |             |       |    |        |                     |
| 4.  | T | F | F |         |             |       |    |        |                     |
| 5.  | F | T | T |         |             |       |    |        |                     |
| 6.  | F | T | F |         |             |       |    |        |                     |
| 7.  | F | F | T |         |             |       |    |        |                     |
| 8.  | F | F | F |         |             |       |    |        |                     |

A. For what row(s) is p ⊃ (q ∨ r) False?    _____

B. For what row(s) is (p · q) ≡ (~q · r) True? _____

---

A. p ⊃ (q ∨ r) is False only in row 4.
B. (p · q) ≡ (~q · r) is True in rows 4, 5, 6 and 8.

Next frame.

# 52

Although variables, in general, may "stand for" any sentence of any complexity, we have been using variables to replace *simple* sentences within a compound in order to discover the logical form of the compound sentence.

How do you feel about this procedure?

1. I think I know how to find the *logical form* of a sentence, and if that's all I need to know to accomplish the objectives of this program, I'd like to continue. But could I have a little more practice finding the logical forms of sentences?

2. I see how to find the *logical form* of a sentence, but it seems like a lot of extra work. Why can't I just make a truth table with the actual sentences? Why do I have to make replacements with variables?

3. I'm sorry but I'm still confused about variables and the notion of *logical form*.

Choice 1, turn to page 63.

Choice 2, turn to frame 53.

Choice 3, review material in frames 32–34 and then turn to page 63.

61

# 53

Variables enable us to deal with the modality of *possibility.* Consider some actual compound sentence containing the simple sentence:

S: The temperature of the sun is extremely high.

If we were to consider the truth conditions of the compound sentence without using variables, we should be forced to say something like:

If **S** *were* False, then . . .

Now the subjunctive mood or the concept of contrary-to-fact suppositions is in greater need of clarification than matter-of-fact, declarative assertions. Indeed we hope that the analysis we are learning in this program will be of assistance in clarifying the logic of intensional and modal discourse.

Thus variables allow us to avoid such locutions as: If **S** *were* False, . . . and to say, rather: If **q** *is* False, . . .

A truth table, then, is *not* a catalog of possibilities in some non-actual world, but is instead a catalog of the results of substituting *actual* True or False sentences for variables.

We shall continue, however, to *speak* informally and to use the subjunctive mood where appropriate.

Turn to page 63.

TEAR THIS SHEET OUT / You may use this sheet as your shield. You may also do scratch work on it.

------------------------------------ FOLD HERE ------------------------------------

# 54

Some review is in order before we go on. Fill in the following truth table.

| p | q | (p ∨ q) | (p & q) |
|---|---|---------|---------|
| T | T | T | T |
| T | F | T | F |
| F | T | T | F |
| F | F | F | F |

---

| p | q | (p ∨ q) | (p & q) |
|---|---|---------|---------|
| T | T | T | T |
| T | F | T | F |
| F | T | T | F |
| F | F | F | F |

If you missed any of these, return to frames 33–35 for review and then go to frame 55.

If you are correct, turn to next frame.

# 55

Fill in the truth table:

| p | q | p ⊃ q | p ≡ q |
|---|---|-------|-------|
| T | T | T | T |
| T | F | F | F |
| F | T | T | F |
| F | F | T | T |

---

| p | q | p ⊃ q | p ≡ q |
|---|---|-------|-------|
| T | T | T | T |
| T | F | F | F |
| F | T | T | F |
| F | F | T | T |

If you missed any of these, return to frames 44–48 for review, and then go on to frame 56.

If you are correct, turn to next frame.

# 56

SUMMARY

You have learned about truth functional sentences, whose truth values (either True or False) are determined by the truth values of their component sentences.

There are five common truth functional connectives, several various symbolizations of these, and several various English words that serve to connect sentences into truth functional compound sentences.

The significance of truth functional connections is completely given by the truth table array of truth values.

Finally, parentheses are used to indicate how sentences are to be grouped together. Clearly

$\sim(p \supset q)$     is different from     $(\sim p \supset q)$

| p | q | $(p \supset q)$ | $\sim p$ | $\sim(p \supset q)$ | $(\sim p \supset q)$ |
|---|---|---|---|---|---|
| T | T | T | F | F | T |
| T | F | F | F | T | T |
| F | T | T | T | F | T |
| F | F | T | T | F | F |

Fill in the blanks. Notice that

$\sim(p \supset q)$ is the denial of a conditional, and

$(\sim p \supset q)$ is a conditional whose antecedent is a denial.

Next frame.

# 57

Any compound sentence whose truth value depends only on the truth values of its components can be symbolized by a careful combination of these five connectives. Which connectives to use however is not always indicated by the presence of 'and', 'or', and 'if . . ., then _____'. We must ask ourselves under what conditions the compound would be True or False, and then select our symbols accordingly.

Example:

We shall leave at eight o'clock, *unless* it rains.

    L:  We shall leave at eight o'clock.

    R:  It rains.

Here the truth conditions are not clear. Some people would read this, *weakly*, as:

*If* it does *not* rain, *then* we shall leave at eight o'clock.

which is symbolized:  ~R ⊃ L

Fill in the truth table:

| p | q | ~p | ~p ⊃ q |
|---|---|----|--------|
| T | T |    |        |
| T | F |    |        |
| F | T |    |        |
| F | F |    |        |

---

| p | q | ~p | ~p ⊃ q |
|---|---|----|--------|
| T | T | F  | T      |
| T | F | F  | T      |
| F | T | T  | T      |
| F | F | T  | F      |

If you have made any errors, turn to frame 58.

If this is correct, turn to frame 59.

# 58

Perhaps it's time for a coffee break.

You should have had no trouble in seeing that in (~p ⊃ q), the antecedent is ~p and the consequent is q. The antecedent is T and the consequent F *only* in row 4, and so (~p ⊃ q) is F *only* in row 4.

You might refer back to frame 51 before going on to frame 59.

# 59

We have rephrased **We shall leave at eight o'clock, unless it rains.** as **If it does not rain, then we shall leave at eight o'clock.**

The truth table for sentences whose form is that of **~R ⊃ L** is

|       | p | q | ~p ⊃ q |
|-------|---|---|--------|
| Row 1 | T | T | T |
| Row 2 | T | F | T |
| Row 3 | F | T | T |
| Row 4 | F | F | F |

Now consider those possible worlds where it is True that *it rains* (and False that it does not rain). What can we infer about our leaving at eight o'clock? That is, assuming our compound sentence is True and also that it rains, shall we or shall we not leave at eight o'clock?

Which row (or rows) of the truth table is relevant to this question?

| If you have: | Turn to: |
|--------------|----------|
| row 4 | frame 60. |
| rows 1 and 2 | frame 61. |
| rows 3 and 4 | frame 62. |
| rows 1, 2, and 3 | frame 63. |

# 60

You said row 4 is relevant. Yet in row 4, p is False, contrary to our assumption that the sentence **It rains.** is True.

Notice also that the entire compound sentence is False in row 4, contrary to our other assumption.

THE CORRECT ANSWER CANNOT INCLUDE ROW 4.

Return to frame 59 and choose another answer.

# 61

Rows 1 and 2 are the relevant ones. CORRECT.

The compound sentence is T in these cases and p (It rains) is also T in these cases.

We note that q is T in row 1, and F in row 2. This means **We shall leave at eight o'clock** may be either T or F, and hence it is *undetermined* whether or not we leave at eight o'clock. We may leave at eight o'clock *in spite of the rain.* All we have committed ourselves to in saying, "If it does not rain, then we shall leave at eight o'clock," is IF IT DOES NOT RAIN, THEN WE SHALL SURELY LEAVE AT EIGHT O'CLOCK.

Example continued from frame 57:

Others would take the assertion of **L unless R** in a much stronger sense:

>**We shall leave at eight o'clock *if and only if* it does *not* rain.**
which is symbolized:   (L ≡∼R)

Here, if it does rain, then we shall *not* leave at eight o'clock; the decision has been made.

Which row of the following truth table shows us that if it rains we shall *not* leave at eight o'clock?

*3*

|  | L | R | (L ≡∼R) |
|---|---|---|---|
|  | p | q | p ≡∼q |
| Row 1 | T | T | F |
| Row 2 | T | F | T |
| Row 3 | F | T | T |
| Row 4 | F | F | F |

Turn to frame 64.

# 62

You said rows 3 and 4. In row 4, the *compound* sentence is F, contrary to our assumption!

Also p is a False sentence in these rows. Thus **It rains** is a False sentence in these cases. The question, however, assumed that it was True that it rained.

Return to frame 59 and try a different answer, after you have reviewed the page carefully.

# 63

You said rows 1, 2 and 3. Now, the compound sentence is True in all these cases. *But*, in row 3, the truth value of p is F. We are assuming that **It rains** is True!

Return to frame 59 and figure out a new answer.

# 64

Row 3 represents the case where **L** is False and **R** is True. Hence, this is the situation where it *does* rain and we do *not* leave at eight o'clock.

We have rephrased **L unless R** in two different ways:

$(\sim R \supset L)$          $(L \equiv \sim R)$

Which is the *correct* symbolization of a sentence containing the word 'unless'? Certainly no blanket answer can be given. The word 'unless' is used in both a weak and a strong sense. A similar situation arose with the word 'or'. Only the context or further inquiry can reveal the correct symbolization.

Using the above abbreviations, L and R, circle a correct symbolization of:

        L                            R

We shall leave at eight o'clock whether or not it rains.

1. $L \lor \sim R$                     3. $(R \lor \sim R) \lor L$

2. $L \rightarrow -R$                   4. $(R \lor \sim R) \supset L$

---

4. $(R \lor \sim R) \supset L$

Turn to next frame.

# 65

Circle the formula on the right that correctly symbolizes the English sentence on the left.

Water boils <u>when and only when</u> the temperature is above 100° C and the vapor pressure is less than 76 cm of mercury.

W: Water boils.

T: The temperature is above 100° C.

V: The vapor pressure is less than 76 cm of mercury.

$(T \supset W) \cdot V$

$W \supset (T \cdot V)$

$(W \equiv T) \cdot V$

$\boxed{W \equiv (T \cdot V)}$

---

$W \equiv (T \cdot V)$

If incorrect, turn to frame 66.

If you are correct, turn to frame 67.

# 66

Let's put parentheses around the components of the sentence, and underline connective words.

> (Water boils) <u>when and only when</u> (the temperature is above 100° C) <u>and</u> (the vapor pressure is less than 76 cm of mercury.)

Now replace the English clauses with their abbreviations:

> W <u>when and only when</u> T <u>and</u> V

The sentence asserts that W *when and only when* two conditions are *jointly* met. Thus the major connective is 'when and only when'. Reflection on the truth conditions of this assertion leads to: $W \equiv (T \cdot V)$

Turn to next frame.

# 67

Circle the formula on the right for the English sentence on the left.

Cheating is not morally right, and if Kant is to be believed neither is lying.
- C: Cheating is morally right.
- K: Kant is to be believed.
- L: Lying is morally right.

~(C · (K ⊃ L))

(~C · K) ∨ L

⟨~C · (K ⊃ ~L)⟩

(K ⊃ ~C) · ~L

$$\sim C \cdot (K \supset \sim L)$$

---

~C · (K ⊃ ~L)

If incorrect, turn to next frame.

If you are correct, turn to frame 69.

# 68

Perhaps we should rephrase our given sentence:

> Cheating is not morally right, and if Kant is to be believed neither is lying.

in a more explicit form:

> Cheating is not morally right, and if Kant is to be believed *then lying is not morally right.*

Now place parentheses around the English sentences that are components of this compound:

> (Cheating is not morally right), and if (Kant is to be believed) then (lying is not morally right).

Replacing with abbreviations (and negation signs):

> ~C, and if K, then ~L

This is a conjunction of two statements, **~C** and **If K then ~L**

> ~C · (K ⊃ ~L)

Turn to next frame.

# 69

Circle the formula on the right for the English sentence on the left

Neither rain nor sleet nor hail will stay these couriers.

R: Rain will stay these couriers.

S: sleet " " " "

H: Hail " " "

~R ·~S ·~H

~R ∨ ~S ∨ ~H

~(R · S · H)

~(R ∨ S ∨ H)

~(R · ~S · ~H)

~R · ~ · S · ~ H

---

~R ·~S ·~H     (You could also circle ~(R ∨ S ∨ H) since it asserts essentially the same thing.)

Turn to next frame.

# 70

Are you bothered by the absence of *interior* parentheses?

Whenever there is a sequence of conjunctions (or disjunctions), you can omit the parentheses, because the grouping of the conjuncts (or disjuncts) does not affect the truth value of the compound.

(((p · q) · r) · s)     has the same truth table as (p · (q · (r · s)))

Thus we usually write:     (p · q · r · s)

You may want to *verify* this for the example below.

| p | q | r | ((p ∨ q) ∨ r) | (p ∨ (q ∨ r)) |
|---|---|---|---------------|---------------|
| T | T | T | T | T |
| T | T | F | T | T |
| T | F | T | T | T |
| T | F | F | T | T |
| F | T | T | T | T |
| F | T | F | T | T |
| F | F | T | T | T |
| F | F | F | F | F |

Next frame.

# 71

Truth tables allow us also to determine when two sentences *essentially assert the same thing* in different ways. Two sentences essentially assert the same thing when they are *logically equivalent*. And we have already seen that two sentences are logically equivalent if their truth tables are identical.

Two sentences whose logical forms are p and ~~p are logically equivalent.

| p | ~p | ~~p |
|---|-----|-----|
| T | F | T |
| F | T | F |

Complete the above truth table and the following one for ~(~p ·~q)

| p | q | ~p | ~q | ~p ·~q | ~(~p ·~q) |
|---|---|-----|-----|--------|-----------|
| T | T | F | F | F | T |
| T | F | F | T | F | T |
| F | T | T | F | F | T |
| F | F | T | T | T | F |

What formula, using only one of our basic connectives, is logically equivalent to ~(~p ·~q)?

$\times$   (p∨q)

(Answer.)

Answer in next frame.

# 72

(p ∨ q) has the same truth table as ~(~p · ~q)

(p · q) has the same truth table as ~(~p ∨ ~q)

These pairs of logical equivalences are known as _De Morgan's Laws._

De Morgan's Laws are sometimes given as:

~(p ∨ q) is logically equivalent to (~p · ~q)

~(p · q) is logically equivalent to (~p ∨ ~q)

Now you have learned that (p ⊃ q) is _defined_ as ~(p · ~q). Using De Morgan's Laws find a _disjunction_ to which (p ⊃ q) is logically equivalent.

$$\underline{\qquad (\sim p \lor q) \qquad}$$

---

(p ⊃ q) is logically equivalent to (~p ∨ ~~q) or, using your knowledge of double negation, (~p ∨ q).

Next frame.

# 73

An easy way to state these equivalences in English is:
  (1) The *negation of a conjunction* is the *disjunction of the negations* of the components.
  (2) The *negation of a disjunction* is the *conjunction of the negations* of the components.

These equivalences, or ones quite similar to them, are known as ___De Morgans___ Laws.
(Whose?)

---

De Morgan's Laws

---

For example:  ~(B ∨ H)    $\sim B \cdot \sim H$
  B: Beer is served.
  H: The men are happy.

Interpretation:   It is not the case that beer is served or the men are happy.

Using both De Morgan's Laws and simple reflection, you should be able to see that this means the same thing as:

___Beer isn't served___ and ___the men aren't happy___
(Fill in the English sentences.)

---

Beer is *not* served *and* the men are *not* happy.

# 74

Some logical equivalences are trivial:

(p ∨ q) is logically equivalent to (q ∨ p)

Others require some transformation according to remembered logical equivalences, or an appeal to truth tables.

Problem:
(p ⊃ q) is logically equivalent to which of the following? Use the truth table this time.

(−p ⊃ −q)          (−q ⊃ −p)

| p | q | (p ⊃ q) | −p | −q | (−p ⊃ −q) | (−q ⊃ −p) |
|---|---|---------|----|----|-----------|-----------|
| T | T | T | F | F | T | T |
| T | F | F | F | T | T | F |
| F | T | T | T | F | F | T |
| F | F | T | T | T | T | T |

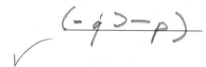

(−q ⊃ −p)

✓

Next frame.

# 75

| p | q | (p ⊃ q) | ~p | ~q | (~q ⊃ ~p) |
|---|---|---------|----|----|-----------|
| T | T | T | F | F | T |
| T | F | F | F | T | F |
| F | T | T | T | F | T |
| F | F | T | T | T | T |

Since (−q ⊃ −p) is logically equivalent to (p ⊃ q), we can see how:

If cows cannot whistle, then pigs cannot fly.

says in a different way:

If pigs can fly, then cows can whistle.

The formula (−q ⊃ −p) is often called the *contrapositive* form of the formula (p ⊃ q).

In interpreting symbolic formulae into English sentences, it is a good idea to stick as closely as possible to a literal translation of the symbolic connectives. The awkward and stylistically painful English sentence that usually results can then be rephrased into a more acceptable form.

**S ⊃ (L ⊃ E)** is more correctly interpreted by which numbered English sentence below? Check one.

S: The switch is on.
L: The lever is thrown.
E: An explosion results.

1. If when the switch is on, the lever is thrown, then an explosion results.

2. If the switch is on, then when the lever is thrown, an explosion results.

Turn to next frame.

# 76

Sentence 2, **If the switch is on, then when the lever is thrown, an explosion results.**, or **S → (L → E)**, is logically equivalent to which one of these:

a. (S · L) → E

b. (S → L) → E

| p | q | r | p · q | p → q | q → r | p → (q → r) | (p · q) → r | (p → q) → r |
|---|---|---|---|---|---|---|---|---|
| T | T | T |  |  | T |  |  |  |
| T | T | F |  |  | F |  |  |  |
| T | F | T |  |  | T |  |  |  |
| T | F | F |  |  | T |  |  |  |
| F | T | T |  |  |  |  |  |  |
| F | T | F |  |  |  |  |  |  |
| F | F | T |  |  |  |  |  |  |
| F | F | F |  |  |  |  |  |  |

a. (S · L) → E    If the columns under 'p → (q → r)' and '(p · q) → r' are not identical, find your errors and correct them.

Turn to next frame.

# 77

A sentence of the form

$$p \rightarrow (q \rightarrow r)$$

is logically equivalent to one of the form

$$(p \cdot q) \rightarrow r$$

What is a correct interpretation of $(S \cdot L) \rightarrow E$?

1. If the switch is on and the lever is thrown, then an explosion results.
2. The switch is on and if the lever is thrown, then an explosion results.

_____/_____

---

1. If the switch is on and the lever is thrown, then an explosion results.

Turn to next frame.

# 78

Circle the English sentence that correctly interprets the formula.

A ⊃ (~B ⊃ C)

A: Acid and water are mixed.
B: You wish to be burned.
C: You should be careful.

1. If acid and water are mixed and you do not wish to be burned, then you should be careful.

2. When acid and water are mixed, you should be careful if you do not wish to be burned.

$(A \cdot {\sim}B) \to C$ ✗

$A \to ({\sim}B \to C)$

If A then (if ~B then C )

C if ~B

Help!

Choice 1, turn to frame 79.

Choice 2, turn to frame 80.

# 79

No!　　**A ⊃ (~B ⊃ C)**　　can be partially interpreted as
**If A, then if ~B then C.**

Furthermore the latter phrase, 'if ~B then C', may be rephrased in several ways, such as:　　~B only if C　　and　　C, if ~B

So one interpretation could be:　　If A, then C if ~B.

More explicitly:

> If acid and water are mixed, then you should be careful if you do not wish to be burned.

This sentence corresponds very closely to 2.

Next frame.

# 80

Sentence 2 is correct. But something puzzling is going on. Let us look at the two answers again.

1. If acid and water are mixed and you do not wish to be burned, then you should be careful.
2. When acid and water are mixed, you should be careful if you do not wish to be burned.

Using the abbreviations given for this example, we symbolize these as:

1. $(A \cdot \sim B) \supset C$
2. $A \supset (\sim B \supset C)$

It is easy (but tiresome) to verify that these two sentences are logically equivalent, that they assert "essentially the same thing"!

It will not do to accept as a correct symbolization *any* sentence logically equivalent to the given one, since one can add on to any formula additional formulae which do not affect the truth values of the original formula. For example, $(p \lor \sim p)$ conjoined to any formula q is logically equivalent to q. Thus, there are an infinite number of structurally different formulae that are logically equivalent to any one formula.

But efforts to restrict the range of acceptable or correct symbolizations of a given sentence have failed to be other than arbitrary.

In symbolizing, therefore, we are guided (intuitively) by the grammatical structure of the original English sentence, and in translating we are again guided by the parentheses and other logical symbols. That is to say, there are no *general* criteria of adequacy for symbolizations or translations, but we must rely on good sense and general agreement.

This is *the* critical problem in *applied* logic.

Next frame.

# 81

Circle the English sentence that correctly interprets the formula.

(P ∨ W) ⊃ (S ·~E)

P: Prices go up.
W: Wages go down.
S: Salaried workers will suffer.
E: Pensioners will suffer.

1. If prices go up then either wages go down or else salaried workers will not suffer, and furthermore pensioners will suffer.

2. If either prices go up or wages go down, then salaried workers will, and pensioners will not, suffer.

3. Either prices go up, or if wages go down then salaried workers will suffer and it is not the case that pensioners will suffer.

(If P or W) then (S + not E)

Choice 1, turn to frame 82.

2, turn to frame 83.

3, turn to frame 84.

# 82

You shouldn't have made this error! Sentence 1 begins:     If prices
go up, then either . . .

   This must have come from a formula that begins:     (P ⊃ . . .

Return to frame 81 and try again.

Sentence 2 is correct!

Determine by truth table analysis which of the following pairs of formulae are logically equivalent:

1.      ~p ≡ (~p ⊃ ~q)          p ≡ (p ⊃ q)

No

| p | q | ~p | ~q | p⊃q | ~p⊃~p | ~p≡(~p⊃~q) | p≡(p⊃q) |
|---|---|----|----|-----|-------|-----------|---------|
| T | T | F | F | T | T | F | T |
| T | F | F | T | F | T | F | F |
| F | T | T | F | T | F | F | F |
| F | F | T | T | T | T | T | F |

2.      ~(p ∨ q)          ~p · ~q

Yes

| p | q | ~p | ~q | p∨q | ~(p∨q) | ~p · ~q |
|---|---|----|----|-----|--------|---------|
| T | T | F | F | T | F | F |
| T | F | F | T | T | F | F |
| F | T | T | F | T | F | F |
| F | F | T | T | F | T | T |

3.      p → (q → p)          ~p → (~q → ~p)

yes

| p | q | ~p | ~q | q→p | ~q→~p | p→(q→p) | ~p→(~q→~p) |
|---|---|----|----|-----|-------|---------|------------|
| T | T | F | F | T | T | T | T |
| T | F | F | T | T | F | T | T |
| F | T | T | F | F | F | T | T |
| F | F | T | T | T | T | T | T |

The pairs in numbers _____ and _____ are logically equivalent
(Fill in.)

| If you have: | Turn to: |
|---|---|
| 1 and 2 | frame 85. |
| 1 and 3 | frame 87. |
| 2 and 3 | frame 88. |

# 84

Sentence 3 is not correct. It comes from the sentence:

$$P \lor (W \supset (S \cdot \sim E))$$

Watch your parentheses. Return to frame 81.

# 85

No. Perhaps your truth tables were constructed carelessly. The items in 2 *are* logically equivalent.

Re-do the truth tables for 1 and 3.

1.    ~p ≡ (~p ⊃~q)          p ≡ (p ⊃ q)

| p | q | ~p | ~q | ~p ⊃~q | ~p ≡ (~p ⊃~q) | p ⊃ q | p ≡ (p ⊃ q) |
|---|---|----|----|--------|----------------|-------|--------------|
| T | T |    |    |        |                |       |              |
| T | F |    |    |        |                |       |              |
| F | T |    |    |   F    |                |       |      F       |
| F | F |    |    |        |                |       |              |

Biconditional             compare

3.      p → (q → p)        ~p → (~q →~p)

| p | q | q → p | p → (q → p) | ~p | ~q | ~q →~p | ~p → (~q →~p) |
|---|---|-------|-------------|----|----|--------|----------------|
| T | T |   T   |      T      | F  | F  |   T    |       T        |
| T | F |   T   |      T      | F  | T  |   F    |       T        |
| F | T |   F   |      T      | T  | F  |   T    |       T        |
| F | F |   T   |      T      | T  | T  |   T    |       T        |

Are the items in 3 logically equivalent?       Yes / No

Yes. Turn to frame 88.

No. Turn to frame 86.

# 86

No. You had better go back over the use of tables to determine logical equivalence.

Review the material in frames 71–77.

Then re-work *all* the problems from frame 83 in the space allowed in this frame. Choose the correct answer in frame 83 and follow the directions for that choice.

1.     $\sim p \equiv (\sim p \supset \sim q)$          $p \equiv (p \supset q)$

2.     $\sim (p \lor q)$          $\sim p \cdot \sim q$

3.     $p \rightarrow (q \rightarrow p)$          $\sim p \rightarrow (\sim q \rightarrow \sim p)$

# 87

Incorrect. The items in 3 *are* logically equivalent.
  Re-do the truth tables for 1 and 2.

1.      ~p ≡ (~p ⊃ ~q)                    p ≡ (p ⊃ q)

| p | q | ~p | ~q | ~p ⊃ ~q | ~p ≡ (~p ⊃ ~q) | p ⊃ q | p ≡ (p ⊃ q) |
|---|---|----|----|---------|----------------|-------|-------------|
| T | T |    |    |         |                |       |             |
| T | F |    |    |         |                |       |             |
| F | T |    |    |    F    |                |       |      F      |
| F | F |    |    |         |                |       |             |

                        Biconditional              compare

2.      ~(p ∨ q)                ~p ·~q

| p | q | p ∨ q | ~(p ∨ q) | ~p | ~q | ~p ·~q |
|---|---|-------|----------|----|----|--------|
|   |   |       |          |    |    |        |
|   |   |       |          |    |    |        |
|   |   |       |          |    |    |        |
|   |   |       |          |    |    |        |

Are the items in 2 logically equivalent?                    Yes / No

Yes.  Turn to frame 88.
No.  Turn back to frame 86.

# 88

The items in 2 and 3 are logically equivalent.

2.    ~(p V q)              ~p ·~q

| p | q | p V q | ~(p V q) | ~p | ~q | ~p ·~q |
|---|---|-------|----------|----|----|--------|
| T | T | T | F | F | F | F |
| T | F | T | F | F | T | F |
| F | T | T | F | T | F | F |
| F | F | F | T | T | T | T |

3.    p → (q → p)              ~p → (~q →~p)

| p | q | q → p | p → (q → p) | ~p | ~q | ~q →~p | ~p → (~q →~p) |
|---|---|-------|-------------|----|----|--------|---------------|
| T | T | T | T | F | F | T | T |
| T | F | T | T | F | T | F | T |
| F | T | F | T | T | F | T | T |
| F | F | T | T | T | T | T | T |

Turn to page 100.

# Part I Review with Comments

(1) You should be able to select from a list of symbols those symbols which are most commonly used for the five major logical connectives.

*Comment:* (a) You will often find the symbol for the <u>conditional</u> called the symbol for <u>*material implication*</u>. (Also the biconditional is called <u>*material equivalence*</u>.) These names are traditional but misleading.

(b) In Part II, we shall use just one of each of the symbols you have learned.

(2) You should be able to construct truth tables for each of the five major connectives.

*Comment:* This is easy if you remember the truth conditions for each connective:

(i) The denial of p is True if p is False, otherwise False.

(ii) The conjunction of p and q is True if both p and q are True, otherwise False.

(iii) The disjunction of p and q is False if both p and q are False, otherwise True.

(iv) The conditional with antecedent p and consequent q is False if p is True and q False, otherwise True.

(v) The biconditional of p and q is True if both p and q are True or both False, otherwise False.

(3) You should be able to recognize when a symbolic formula correctly exhibits the logical form of an English sentence.

*Comment:* In English, the kind of connective is usually clear, but the grouping of components can be quite ambiguous. It is necessary to insure that the parentheses in the formula group together the correct components, and the major connective of the formula is the major connective of the English sentence.

Ambiguous English sentence:

If it rains the picnic is cancelled and the Club closes at six.

There are two possible symbolizations of this:

$R \supset (P \cdot C)$ $\qquad\qquad$ $(R \supset P) \cdot C$

(4) You should be able to reconstruct an English sentence given a symbolic formula and the sentence abbreviations.

*Comment:* If worse comes to worse you could scratch out the connective symbols and write in 'and', 'if. . . ., then ', and so on. In polishing up the style of the resulting English sentence, be careful that you do not change the truth conditions.

An example of how one might go WRONG is:  ¬(Q & R)

> Q: The Queen arrives.
> R: John remains seated.

(i)  It is not the case Q and R.

(ii)  The Queen does not arrive and John remains seated. WRONG

(ii)  *should be*, as you know:    It is not the case that *both* the Queen arrives and John remains seated.

(5) You should be able to determine when two formulae are logically equivalent.

Comment:  The sentential calculus is a simple system to work with because it is so easy to determine if (and if not) two formulae are logically equivalent. To determine this you see if the truth tables for the two formulae are identical. This can *always* be done.

For example, are p → (q → p) and q → (p → q) logically equivalent? Draw up a truth table and see.

| p | q | p → q | q → p | p → (q → p) | q → (p → q) |
|---|---|-------|-------|-------------|-------------|
| T | T | T | T | T | T |
| T | F | F | T | T | T |
| F | T | T | F | T | T |
| F | F | T | T | T | T |

With experience you will recognize that one formula can be *transformed* into another by substituting some common logical equivalences, such as:

| | | |
|---|---|---|
| Double Negation | ~~p | p |
| De Morgan's Laws | ~(p ∨ q) | ~p · ~q |
| | ~(p · q) | ~p ∨ ~q |
| Contraposition | p ⊃ q | ~q ⊃ ~p |
| Exportation | (p · q) ⊃ r | p ⊃ (q ⊃ r) |

Thus one might use a sequence of transformations, each formula of the sequence being logically equivalent to the preceding one, and hence, each being equivalent to any of the others.

p ⊃ (−q ∨ r)

| | |
|---|---|
| −(−q ∨ r) ⊃ −p | by Contraposition |
| (− −q · −r) ⊃ −p | De Morgan |
| (q · −r) ⊃ −p | Double negation |
| (−r · q) ⊃ −p | (Commutativity) |
| −r ⊃ (q ⊃ −p) | Exportation |
| −r ⊃ −(q · − −p) | (Definition) |
| −r ⊃ −(q · p) | Double negation |
| (q · p) ⊃ r | Contraposition |
| (p · q) ⊃ r | (Commutativity) |

101

All of these are equivalent, but to show the first equivalent to the last, you could use truth tables to settle the issue. You can always use truth tables to determine logical equivalence.

$$\sim (p \lor q) \qquad (\sim p \cdot \sim q)$$

$$A \supset (-q \lor r)$$

1 Contrap

$$1.\ \sim(-q \lor r) \supset \sim A$$

De Morgans
Double negative

$$2.\ (\sim q \cdot \sim r) \supset \sim A$$

$$3.\ (q \cdot \sim r) \supset \sim A$$

Exportation

$$4.\ q \supset (\sim r \supset \sim A)$$

$$5.\ q \supset ($$

# PART II THE PREDICATE CALCULUS WITH IDENTITY (PCI)

## Objectives

Upon completion you should be able to:

(1) Select the symbolic formula of PCI that correctly symbolizes an English sentence of moderate complexity.

(2) Select an English sentence that correctly interprets a given formula of PCI of moderate complexity.

(3) Recognize some elementary logical equivalences between formulae of PCI.

(4) Recognize some elementary contradictories of given formulae of PCI.

(5) Interpret an expression containing the abstraction operator.

TEAR THIS SHEET OUT / You may use this sheet as your shield.
You may also do scratch work on it.

----------------------------------- FOLD HERE ------------------------------------------

105

# 89

While it is basic and fundamental, the analysis of truth functional compound sentences is usually not fine enough for our purposes.

> Ludwig is a dog.

and

> Rover is a dog.

are clearly similar sentences, yet this similarity is lost when we abbreviate them **L** and **R** respectively.

> Ludwig is small.

and

> Ludwig is brown.

are also sentences whose similarity is lost when we use **S** and **B** respectively as abbreviations.

All four of our example sentences are simple, but what is the major similarity between the sentences **S** and **B** which is not also shared by the sentences **L** and **R**?

S & B have the same subject, Ludwig

(Write your answer.)

---

**B** and **S** have the same *subject*, Ludwig.

Next frame.

# 90

We shall abbreviate the *subject terms* in a sentence with *lower case letters* from the beginning of the alphabet:

a, b, c, . . ., l, m are *individual constants*

So, **Ludwig is brown.** becomes **l is brown.** and **Ludwig is small.** becomes **l is small.**

Work out the unfinished examples below:
1. Rover is a dog.
    e:  Rover.

e is a dog.

2. Charles did not steal the Rembrandt from the Louvre.
    c:  Charles.
    b:  the Rembrandt.
    l:  the Louvre.

c did not steal b from l

3. Barbara is a tall, thin blonde.
    b:  Barbara.

b is a tall, thin blonde

---

3. b is a tall, thin blonde.

---

4. Fielding wrote *Tom Jones* but not *Moll Flanders*.
    f:  Fielding.
    j:  *Tom Jones.*
    m:  *Moll Flanders.*

f wrote j but not m

---

4. f wrote j but not m.

*continued*

5. If Tom and Jerry are elected, then Larry has done his work well.
    m: Tom.
    j:  Jerry.
    l:  Larry

    *If m and j are elected then l has done his work well.*

---

5. If m and j are elected, then l has done his work well.

Next frame.

# 91

1. (a) Fielding wrote *Tom Jones* but not *Moll Flanders*.
   (b) Fielding wrote *Tom Jones* but FIELDING did not write *Moll Flanders*.

2. (a) Barbara is a blonde or else she has dyed her hair again.
   (b) Barbara is a blonde or else BARBARA has dyed her hair again.

3. (a) Romeo and Juliet love each other.
   (b) Romeo loves Juliet and Juliet loves Romeo.

Make the subject (or subjects) explicit in the remaining examples.

4. (a) If Tom is drinking champagne, then he has won the race.

   (b) <u>*If Tom is drinking Champagne then Tom has won the race.*</u>

---

4. (b) If Tom is drinking champagne, then Tom has won the race.

---

5. (a) Either Carol and Lois have both passed, or they have failed.

   (b) <u>*Either Carol & Lois have both passed, or Carol + Lois have failed*</u>

---

5. (b) Either Carol and Lois have both passed, or Carol and Lois have failed.

---

6. (a) The Van Gogh has been repaired but not restored.

   (b) <u>*The Van Gogh has been repaired but the Van Gogh has not been restored*</u>

---

6. (b) The Van Gogh has been repaired but the Van Gogh has not been restored.

Next frame.

# 92

Once a sentence has been rephrased so as to make the subjects explicit, you can then replace the names by the *individual constants* which are their abbreviations. Thus,

Fielding wrote *Tom Jones* but not *Moll Flanders.*

would look like:

f wrote j but f did not write m.

What would these look like?

1. Romeo and Juliet love *each other.*
    e: Romeo.
    j: Juliet.

*e loves j and j loves e.*

---

e loves j and j loves e.

---

2. Either Lois and Carol have decided not to come, or they have missed the plane.
    l: Lois.
    c: Carol.

*Either l & c have decided not to come or l & c have missed the plane*

---

Either l and c have decided not to come, or l and c have missed the plane.

Next frame.

# 93

Let's try to rephrase sentences in such a way that we do not have multiple subjects. That is, let us try to have one subject for each *predicate*.

Hence let us rewrite **I and c have missed the plane.** as **I has missed the plane and c has missed the plane.**

Some examples:

1. (a) Either d or j was elected.
   (b) Either d was elected or j was elected.

2. (a) c selected e, f, and g.

   (b)  c selected e, c selected f and c selected g

---

2. (b) c selected e and c selected f and c selected g.

---

3. (a) k and I are each harder than m.

   (b) 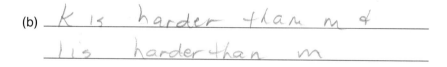 k is harder than m & I is harder than m

---

3. (b) k is harder than m and I is harder than m.

Next frame.

# 94

These examples have been easy, but you must exercise caution in splitting up subjects. Sometimes the sense of the *predicate* demands that the subjects be kept together.

>k and b are twins.

should *not* be written:

>k is a twin and b is a twin.

Also, if I and c *each* bought a dress, we would write:

>I bought a dress and c bought a dress.

*but* if they pooled their money and bought one dress for both of them, we would write:

>I and c (jointly) bought a dress.

Circle the sentence where the subjects very definitely ought *not* to be split up:

1. h and k joined the party later.
2. d and g were tied for second prize.
3. m, k, and I are famous scientists.
4. j stole e and f.

---

2. d and g were tied for second prize.

Next frame.

# 95

You will recall that we said **Ludwig is a dog.** and **Rover is a dog.** were similar sentences. One important similarity between these sentences is that they *assert the same thing about different individuals.*

| Sentences | Predicates |
|---|---|
| 1. Ludwig is a dog. | _L_ is a dog. |
| 2. Romeo loves Juliet. | _R_ loves _J_. |
| 3. Jim gave the pin to Mary. | _J_ gave _P_ to _M_. |

How do we obtain the *predicate* of a simple sentence like those above?

*Delete subject terms*

(Write out the answer.)

---

(In your own words) Delete the subject terms or names from the sentence.

Next frame.

# 96

Another way of looking at the matter is this. When all the *blanks* in a predicate are filled with *names*, we obtain a *sentence*.

So when the predicate _____ **is a dog.** has a name placed in the blank, we have a sentence. If the name is 'Fido' (abbreviated: f) we have the *True* sentence **f is a dog.**, and if the name is 'George Washington' (abbreviated: g) we have the *False* sentence **g is a dog.**

     _____ is a small, brown, noisy dog.

can be rephrased as

     _____ is small and _____ is brown and _____ is noisy and _____ is a dog.

Some of the eight predicates below are *complex*, and can be resolved into a sequence of simpler predicates joined by such connectives as 'or', 'and', etc. Circle the *complex* predicates.

1. _____ struck _____.

2. Tall, lean _____ struck short, fat _____.

3. _____ has blue eyes and blonde hair.

4. _____ has a peculiar nose.

5. _____ is much greater than _____.

6. _____ has more courage or less brains than _____.

7. _____ is between _____ and _____.

8. _____ very nearly matches _____ in color.

---

2. Tall, lean _____ struck short, fat _____.
3. _____ has blue eyes and blonde hair.
6. _____ has more courage or less brains than _____.

If you are correct, go to frame 98.

If you are incorrect, turn to next frame.

# 97

Let us look at some of the examples more closely.

2. **Tall, lean _____ struck short, fat _____.** can be rephrased as: **_____ is tall and _____ is lean and _____ struck _____ and _____ is short and _____ is fat.**

4. **_____ has a peculiar nose.** can*not* be rephrased as **_____ is peculiar and _____ has a nose.**

We can admit that further *esthetic* analysis may reveal those properties that make it a peculiar nose, yet *logically*, and with no more context specified, having a peculiar nose is a simple property.

6. **_____ has more courage or less brains than _____.** can be analyzed into: **_____ has more courage than _____ or _____ has less brains than _____.**

7. **_____ is between _____ and _____** is as simple a predicate as one can find. No one thing, or pair of things, is claimed to have a property, or to exemplify a relation. Only a triplet of individuals could exemplify the simple relation denoted by the simple predicate.

Next frame.

# 98

Before we go on, you may wish to review the things you have learned.

Subjects are sometimes implicit and unnamed, and sometimes referred to by pronouns. You should know how to rewrite a sentence to make explicit all subject terms.

Make the subject terms explicit.

1. John hit the ball and trotted to first base.

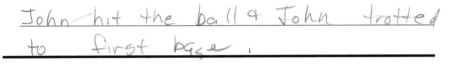

*John hit the ball & John trotted to first base.*

1. John hit the ball and *John* trotted to first base.

2. If he knows what he is doing, Bill is unlikely to receive a shock.

*If Bill knows what Bill is doing, Bill is unlikely to receive a shock*

2. If *Bill* knows what *Bill* is doing, Bill is unlikely to receive a shock.

If you are unclear or have made a mistake, review the material in frame 91.

Otherwise turn to the next frame.

# 99

Explicit subject terms can be replaced by abbreviations (lower case letters from the beginning of the alphabet called *individual constants*.)

But some sentences contain *multiple* subject terms and some contain *complex* predicates. We usually must rephrase such sentences. Simplify and use abbreviations in the following examples:

1. Ludwig and Fido are brown dogs.
   - l: Ludwig.
   - f: Fido.

*No Pronoun*

l is brown and l is a dog and f is brown and f is a dog.

2. Either Betty or Carol spilled the milk and did not wipe it up.
   - b: Betty.
   - c: Carol.
   - m: the milk.

*Either b spilled the m & b did not wipe m up, or c spilled the m & c did not wipe m up*

2. (Either) b spilled m and b did not wipe m up, or c spilled m and c did not wipe m up.

3. Ken is conceited and egotistical, unless Henry is sadly mistaken about him.
   - k: Ken.
   - h: Henry.

*Ken is conceinted unless h is sadly mistaken & k is ego l*

*K is conceited & k is egotistical unless h is sadly mistaken*

3. k is conceited and k is egotistical, unless h is sadly mistaken about k.

Next frame.

118

# 100

We are now going to put capital letters to a new use. *Capital letters except 'F', 'G' and 'H', will be used to abbreviate predicates.*

Returning to our good friend Fido, if

> D: _____ is a dog.
> f: Fido.

then the abbreviation of the sentence **Fido is a dog** is:

$$\overline{\qquad\qquad\qquad\qquad\qquad} \quad \text{Df}$$

1. Fido is faithful.
   > A: _____ is faithful.

$$\overline{\qquad\qquad\qquad\qquad\qquad} \quad \text{Af}$$

2. Ludwig is a dog.
   > l: Ludwig.

$$\overline{\qquad\qquad\qquad\qquad\qquad} \quad \text{Dl}$$

3. Ludwig is a faithful dog.

$$\overline{\qquad\qquad\qquad\qquad\qquad} \quad \text{Dl and Al}$$

4. If Green did not commit the murder, then he is absolutely innocent.
   > C: _____ committed the murder.
   > I: _____ is absolutely innocent.
   > g: Green.

$$\overline{\qquad\qquad\qquad} \quad \text{If not Cg then Ig}$$

Complete the examples:

5. If Charles is foolhardy, he is not a hero.
   > L: _____ is foolhardy.
   > E: _____ is a hero.
   > c: Charles.

*If Lc then not Ec*

---

5. If Lc, not Ec.

Frame 100 continued.

*continued*

6. Alice and Betty are tall blondes.
      a: Alice.
      b: Betty.
      T: _____ is tall.
      B: _____ is a blonde.

*Ta and Tb and Ba and Bb*

---

6. Ta and Ba and Tb and Bb.    (Any order of these four is correct: e.g., Ta and Tb and Ba and Bb.)

If you wish more discussion of these examples, go to frame 101.

Otherwise, go to frame 102.

# 101

In the example,

> If Charles is foolhardy, he is not a hero.

we should first replace the pronoun with the name of the individual referred to.

> If Charles is foolhardy, Charles is not a hero.

We can now abbreviate names with some individual constants.

> If c is foolhardy, c is not a hero.
>
> **c is foolhardy.** is abbreviated: Lc
> **c is a hero.** is abbreviated: Ec

The denial of **Ec** is **not Ec** and so we have:

> If Lc, not Ec

The next example,

> Alice and Betty are tall blondes.

exemplifies both a multiple subject and a complex predicate. First we note that the same (complex) property—the property of being a tall blonde—is predicated of both Alice and Betty. Abbreviating their names, we write:

> a is a tall blonde and b is a tall blonde.

Decomposing the complex predicate _____ **is a tall blonde.** we write:

> a is tall and a is a blonde and b is tall and b is a blonde.

Now we abbreviate these predicates, obtaining:

> Ta and Ba and Tb and Bb

Next frame.

# 102

As long as we deal only in simple properties involving only simple subjects, we could get along with the abbreviatory devices we have been using. For example, D: _____ is a dog.

But when we turn to *relations* obtaining between two or more subjects (formally, predicates with two or more blanks), the situation is different. The abbreviations of predicates must show the *number* and *order* of the blanks in the original predicate.

After all, two *is* less than twelve, and we should make a serious mistake if we changed the order of the numerals in the symbolization of the sentence **Two is less than twelve.**

1. John loves Mary, but Mary doesn't love him.
   L(1)(2): (1) loves (2).
       j: John.
       m: Mary.

   <u>       Ljm but not Lmj       </u>

2. The blue car is between the red car and the truck.
   B(1)(2)(3): (1) is between (2) and (3).
           b: the blue car.
           d: the red car.
           k: the truck.

   <u>       Bbdk           </u>

Using the above abbreviations, symbolize:

3. John loves Mary and Carol.
       c: Carol.

   <u>   Ljm & Ljc   </u>

---

3. Ljm and Ljc

---

4. The truck is between the red car and the blue car.

   <u>   Bk d b   </u>

---

4. Bkdb

Next frame.

# 103

The numerals in the abbreviated predicate (the capital letter) correspond, in specific order, to the blanks in the *unabbreviated predicate*. When symbolizing you should take care to have the *abbreviated names* in the correct order, and when interpreting you should take care that the actual names are in the right order when written in the blanks of the predicate.

The symbolic formula **Cmj** can be interpreted by which *two* of the English sentences?

C(1)(2): (1) called (2).

    m: Mike.

    j: Jane.

1. Jane was called by Mike.
2. Mike was called by Jane.
3. Jane called Mike.
4. Mike called Jane.

_____

**Cmj** may be interpreted as 4. Mike called Jane. *and* 1. Jane was called by Mike.

Next frame.

# 104

The presence of words such as 'but', 'and', 'or', 'not', etc., should have suggested to you what the next and final step in symbolizing is. We have been conjoining and disjoining and denying sentences all along. So, now we'll use the symbols from Part I.

1. *Fielding* wrote *Tom Jones* but not *Moll Flanders*.
    W(1)(2): (1) wrote (2).
        f: Fielding.
        j: Tom Jones.
        m: Moll Flanders.

    (Wfj but not Wfm)

    (Wfj ·~ Wfm)

2. (Lg ⊃ ~Eg)
    L(1): (1) is foolhardy.
    E(1): (1) is a hero.
      g: George.

    If George is foolhardy, he is not a hero.

3. Lean Cassius stabbed Julius in the stomach or the chest.
        L(1): (1) is lean.
    S(1)(2)(3): (1) stabbed (2) in (3).
            c: Cassius.
            j: Julius.
            m: Julius's stomach.
            h: Julius's chest.

    Lc · (Scjm ∨ Scjh)

(A semi-literal rendition of this formula might be: Cassius is lean and either he stabbed Julius in the stomach or he stabbed Julius in the chest.)

124

4. $(Sb \cdot Rb \cdot Db \cdot Bb)$
    $S(1)$: (1) is small.
    $R(1)$: (1) is red.
    $D(1)$: (1) is a dog.
    $B(1)$: (1) barks at strangers.
        b: Bowser.

*Bowser is small + red + a dog + barks at stranger*

(Render into decent English.)

---

4. A good English interpretation is: Bowser is a small, red dog who barks at strangers.

If you have nothing like the correct answer, or are somewhat weak on this material, turn to next frame.

If you are correct and wish to go on, turn to frame 106.

# 105

We are attempting to rephrase complicated sentences as truth functional compounds of *elementary sentences.* Elementary sentences, so far, are one-place predicates with one name in the blank, or two-place predicates with two names in the blanks, and so on. Elementary sentences are abbreviated by one-place predicate letters followed by one individual constant, two-place predicate letters followed by two individual constants, and so on.

When we approach a sentence such as:

> If Bill is guilty, he will be fined or given a warning by the judge.

we first make the subject terms explicit in every instance:

> If Bill is guilty, Bill will be fined by the judge or Bill will be given a warning by the judge.

As far as the *sentential* symbolism is concerned, this has the form:

> p ⊃ (q ∨ r)

We want now to analyze the sentences p, q, and r into their subject-predicate form.

The antecedent of the conditional is: **Bill is guilty.**, which is symbolized (with obvious abbreviations):

> Lb        (We are saving 'F', 'G', and 'H')

The consequent of the conditional is a disjunction, and the left-hand side (the left disjunct) is: **Bill will be fined by the judge.**

Let N(1)(2) mean that the first named individual is fined by the second individual; that is,

> (1) is fined by (2)

Then **Bill is fined by the judge.** is symbolized: Nbj

And by the same sort of passive construction, the right-hand disjunct is symbolized: Wbj

Our completed symbolization looks like this:

> Lb ⊃ (Nbj ∨ Wbj)

Next frame.

# 106

Circle the formula symbolizing the given English sentence.

1. If John is taller than Mary, then if Mary is taller than Ann, John is taller than Ann.

    T(1)(2): (1) is taller than (2).
    
    j: John.
    m: Mary.
    a: Ann.

    Tj ⊃ (Tm ⊃ Ta)

    ⟨Tjm ⊃ (Tma ⊃ Tja)⟩

    Tjm ⊃ (Tam · Tja)

    Tmj ⊃ (Tma ⊃ Tja)

---

1. Tjm ⊃ (Tma ⊃ Tja)

---

2. •Either Jim stole the necklace, or he hasn't an alibi.

    S(1)(2): (1) stole (2).
    
    A(1): (1) has an alibi.
    
    j: Jim.
    e: the necklace.

    Sje ∨ ~Ah

    Sje ∨ Aj

    Sej ∨ Aj

    ⟨Sje ∨ ~Aj⟩

---

2. Sje ∨ ~Aj

Frame 106 continued.

*continued*

3. Lean, hungry Cassius stabbed fat Julius.
      L(1): (1) is lean.
      U(1): (1) is hungry.
      A(1): (1) is fat.
        c: Cassius.
        j: Julius.
  S(1)(2): (1) stabbed (2).

$$S(Lc \cdot Uc), Aj$$

$$Lc \cdot Uc\ S\ Aj$$

$$Lc \cdot Uc \cdot Aj \cdot Scj$$

$$(Lc \cdot Uc) \supset (Scj \cdot Aj)$$

Help

$Lc \cdot Uc \cdot Aj \cdot Scj$

---

3. $Lc \cdot Uc \cdot Aj \cdot Scj$

Next frame.

128

# 107

Circle the English sentence that interprets the given formula.

Kga ⊃ (Pa ·~Am)

K(1)(2): (1) kissed (2).
P(1): (1) is pleased.
A(1): (1) is happy.
g: George.
a: Alice.
m: Mary.

1. Alice is pleased and Mary is not happy, if George kissed Alice.

2. If George kissed Alice, then Alice is pleased only if Mary is unhappy.

---

1. Alice is pleased and Mary is not happy, if George kissed Alice.

---

Tbb ·~Sbd

T(1)(2): (1) talks to (2).
S(1)(2): (1) speaks to (2).
b: Bill.
d: Dr. Nertz.

1. Bill talks and he says nothing to Dr. Nertz.

2. Bill talks to Bill but refuses to speak to Dr. Nertz.

3. Bill talks to himself, but he does not speak to Dr. Nertz.

---

3. Bill talks to himself, but he does not speak to Dr. Nertz.

Page 131.

129

Individual constants: a, b, c, . . ., m
Predicates: A, B, C, D, E, I, J, K, . . .

------------------------------------- FOLD HERE -----------------------------------------

# 108

When we fill in the blanks of a predicate with names of individuals we obtain a sentence. But many sentences have *no* names occurring in them.

> There are some dogs that do not bark.
> All human beings are mortal.
> If anyone falls asleep, he will answer to no one.

To symbolize such sentences we need to use a device (attributed to Bertrand Russell) commonly called a *sentential function* (or *propositional function*).

Using *individual variables*:     u, v, w, x, y, z,     we *construct sentential functions from predicates.*

| PREDICATE | SENTENTIAL FUNCTION |
|---|---|
| (1) is a dog | x is a dog. |
| (1) answers to (2) | x answers to y. |
| (1) is a human being | x is a human being. |

Choose from the right-hand column the appropriate term for the item on the left.

1. Rover is a dog.   *Sentence*     ~~Individual name~~

2. m.   ~~Indiv~~ *constant*     ~~Individual variable~~

3. y is a dog.   *Sentential func.*   ~~Sentence~~ ✓

4. Ludwig.   *Indiv ~~constant~~ name*     ~~Predicate~~ ✓

5. (1) is a dog.   *Predicate*     Sentential function ✓

6. x.   ~~Indiv~~ *indiv.-var* ✓     Individual constant

---

1. Sentence
2. Individual constant (frame 90)
3. Sentential function

4. Individual name
5. Predicate (frames 95, 102)
6. Individual variable

*a — m indiv constants*

Next frame.

133

# 109

The abbreviation of a sentential function is, as you would expect, the abbreviation of the predicate followed by the appropriate individual variables.

| SENTENTIAL FUNCTION | SYMBOLIZED |
|---|---|
| x is a dog | Dx |
| x answers to y | Axy |
| x is a human being | Bx |

You will find some authors writing a two-place predicate symbol *between* the two terms belonging to it. For instance, in mathematics you will find: $x < y$ for **x is less than y.** Later we shall occasionally adopt this way of symbolizing, but for the present we shall write **L x y** for **x is less than y.** Writing the predicate symbol between the terms is awkward when more than two terms are involved.

**x is between y and z** in our notation is:     Bxyz
but some authors are forced to write **xBy; z** or **yBz(x)** or some other confusing symbolization.

One way to construct a *sentence* from a sentential *function* is to replace the individual <u>v a r i a b l e s</u> by individual <u>n a m e s</u>. (Fill in the blanks.)

---

variables; names.

Next frame.

# 110

Suppose we write:

> For some individual x, x is a dog and x barks.

which is symbolized, so far, as:

> For some individual x, (Dx · Bx)

What shall we call such an expression? Noting that what we have written makes an assertion, or in other words, is either True or False, we conclude that this is a *sentence*.

If there were *no dogs that barked*, all the following sentences would be *False*:

> (1) Some dogs bark.
> (2) There are dogs that bark.
> (3) There are some dogs that bark.
> (4) There is at least one dog that barks.

In spite of the fact that the first three of these sentences *suggest* that there exist more than one barking dog, we shall understand them in the minimal sense of (4): *There is at least one x such that x is a dog and x barks.*

Consider these abbreviations:

> j: Johnny.
> Lxy: x loves y.

Complete 2 in the same way as 1.

1. Johnny loves someone.
   (a) j loves someone.
   (b) There is an x such that j loves x.
   (c) There is an x such that Ljx.

2. Someone loves Johnny.
   (a) Someone loves j.
   (b) There is an x such that ___x loves j___
   (c) ___There is an x such that Lxj___

---

2  (b) There is an x such that *x loves j.*
2  (c) *There is an x such that Lxj.*

Next frame.

# 111

To symbolize the concept of there *existing* at least one thing that satis-fies a sentential function, we write a backwards 'E', so:

(∃x)(Dx · Bx)

symbolizes **There is at least one x such that x is a dog and x barks.**

(∃x)(Ljx): Johnny loves someone.
(∃x)(Lxj): Someone loves Johnny.

Since the variables merely keep track of the blanks in a predicate, which variable you use is not important. **(∃x)(Dx · Bx)** means exactly the same thing as **(∃y)(Dy · By)**

Using 'y' for the sake of variety, symbolize completely:

Some sailors do *not* drink whiskey.
Sy: y is a sailor.
Dy: y drinks whiskey.

1. For some y, y is a sailor and ___(∃y)(Sy·~Dy)___

2. _____

---

1. y does not drink whiskey.
2. (∃y)(Sy ·~Dy)
   (Don't forget parentheses.)

Next frame.

# 112

A sentential function is *existentially quantified* if it is preceded by an *existential quantifier*, (∃).

Just as our understanding of the connectives was made precise and complete through the study of truth conditions, so here too we must examine the truth conditions of an existential sentence. We have been saving 'F', 'G' and 'H' for this discussion.

'Fx' will represent for us any arbitrary sentential function of x; 'Fy' is that same sentential function with 'y' in place of 'x'; 'Fa' is a sentence formed from that same sentential function with 'a' filling the blanks of the predicates occurring in F. Speaking generally, '(∃x)Fx' is representative of any existentially quantified sentential function of x.

'Fx' is representative of all of the following sentential functions *except one*. Which one is *not* represented by 'Fx'?

1. (Sx ·~Dx)
2. Lxj
3. (Dy · By)
4. (Ax · (Lxm ∨ Lxk))

---

3. **(Dy · By)** is *not* represented by 'Fx' since it is a sentential function of y. It would be represented by 'Fy'.

Next frame.

# 113

If we have a sentence (∃x)Fx under what conditions is it True? And under what conditions is it False?

These questions can be answered in a simple manner which is satisfactory for our purposes in this program.

(∃x)Fx        is *True* if there is *at least one* name, or denoting expression, which, when substituted for 'x' in Fx, yields a True sentence.

(∃x)Fx        is *False* if *every* name and denoting expression, when substituted for 'x' in Fx, yields a False sentence.

Suppose that, as a matter of fact, John loves Mary but not Helen. Then (for Lxy: x loves y; and obvious abbreviations of 'John', 'Mary', and 'Helen')

**Ljm** is True, and **Ljh** is False.

What is the truth value of **(∃x)Ljx**? (Interpreted: John loves someone.)

True / False

True. Go to frame 115.

False. Go to frame 114.

# 114

You said **John loves someone** is False. But one of our assumptions was that John loves Mary! Remember that the sentence (∃x)Fx needs to have only *one* substitution instance of Fx True, for the whole sentence (∃x)Fx to be True. The fact that John does *not* love Helen is really irrelevant.

Review frame 113 and choose
the correct answer.

# 115

**(∃x)Ljx** is True since at least one of the substitution instances of **Ljx** (namely, **Ljm**) is True.

What if *every* substitution instance of **Ljx** were True? That is, what if **Ljm** and **Ljh** are True and similarly for every possible substitution instance—including the case where **Ljj** is True? That would mean that John loves *everything* (including himself).

When *each and every* substitution instance of a sentential function, Fx, is true, we shall say the *universal quantification* of Fx is true.

The universal quantification of Fx is symbolized: (x)Fx

(Some authors use an inverted 'A': (∀x)Fx, where the upside-down 'A' comes from 'all' just as '∃' came from 'exists'.)

(x)Fx is True if every substitution instance of Fx is True.

(x)Fx is False if there is at least one *substitution*

*of x so that Fx is false*

(Complete the statement.)

---

(x)Fx is False if there is at least one substitution instance of Fx which is False.

Next frame.

# 116

(x)Fx can be read a number of ways:
    For all x, Fx
    Each x is such that Fx
    For any arbitrary x, Fx
    Every x is such that Fx

It is True that all Greeks are mortal, yet it would be incorrect to symbolize the sentence

        All Greeks are mortal.
          Rx: x is a Greek.
          Mx: x is mortal.
as: (x)(Rx · Mx)

Why is this incorrect?

Because not every substitution instance _____ *not everyone*

_____ *a Greek!* _____

_____

(Complete.)

---

Because not every substitution instance of **(Rx · Mx)** is a True sentence. For instance, substitution of 'Napoleon' for 'x' yields: Napoleon is Greek *and* he was mortal.

Next frame.

# 117

(x)Fx is true when there are no false substitution instances of Fx.

How are we to symbolize **All Greeks are mortals.**?

Consider under what conditions we would take this sentence to be true. As we go through the entire universe, picking and choosing individuals, *when we find a Greek, he turns out to be a mortal.*

We can restate **All Greeks are mortals.** as:

For *any* individual x, if x is a Greek, then x is a mortal.

What is the symbolization of the rephrased sentence?

Rx: x is a Greek.
Mx: x is a mortal.

1. (∃x)(Rx · Mx)

2. (x)(Rx · Mx)

3. ((x)Rx ⊃ Mx)

4. (x)(Rx ⊃ Mx)

Choice 1, turn to frame 118.

2, turn to frame 119.

3, turn to frame 120.

4, turn to frame 121.

# 118

($\exists$**x**)(**Rx** · **Mx**) is interpreted as: *At least one* Greek is a mortal.

'($\exists$x)' is an *existential* quantifier of 'x'. Our problem however deals with a *universally* quantified sentence.

Review frame 117 and choose another answer.

# 119

We have just finished a discussion showing this can't be the correct answer.

Reread the material on frame 116. Continue the program from there.

# 120

In symbolizing

> For any x, if x is Greek, then x is mortal.

we might write, as a first step,

> For any x, if Rx then Mx.

Notice that the sentential function that is being quantified by 'For any x' is **if Rx then Mx** which is symbolized:     (Rx ⊃ Mx)

Writing in the universal quantification of x, we obtain choice 4:

(x)(Rx ⊃ Mx)     (Note the parentheses!)

In choice 3:     ((x)Rx ⊃ Mx), the sentential function quantified by '(x)' is just 'Rx'. Thus we have a conditional *formula* whose *antecedent* is '(x)Rx' — which is the symbolization of the complete sentence: Everything is Greek.

So choice 3 symbolizes: If *everything is Greek*, then x is mortal. This expression is not a sentence because 'x' is not within the *scope* of the quantifier and one cannot tell if the whole expression is True or False.

In order to show that the individual chosen in the antecedent is the same individual to be chosen in the consequent, we must enclose the whole expression in parentheses before writing the initial quantifier. That makes all free occurrences of the variable within these parentheses fall within the scope of the quantifier.

The scope of a quantifier is the formula occurring immediately to the right of the quantifier:

 (x)(Rx ⊃ Mx)           (x)Rx ⊃ Mx

Go to frame 122.

# 121

**(x)(Rx ⊃ Mx)** is the correct symbolization of:

For any x, *if* x is a Greek, *then* x is a mortal.

Now if you are quite certain why **((x)Rx ⊃ Mx)** (Choice 3) is incorrect, go on to frame 122.

But if you are puzzled about the position of the left parentheses, turn back to frame 120 for a discussion about the *scope* of a quantifier.

# 122

Remembering that for any sentential function, Fx, the sentence

(∃x)Fx is True if *some* substitution instance of Fx is True,

and

(x)Fx is True if *every* substitution instance of Fx is True,

we can symbolize quite easily a great many English sentences. First some fairly uncomplicated ones:

1. All ravens are black.
   Rx: x is a raven.
   Bx: x is black.

$$(x)(Rx \supset Bx)$$

2. Horses and cows are mammals.
   Ox: x is a horse.
   Cx: x is a cow.
   Mx: x is a mammal.

   (For any x, if x is either a horse or cow, then x is a mammal.)

$$(x)((Ox \lor Cx) \supset Mx)$$

Another rephrasing gives: For any x, if x is a horse, then x is a mammal, *and*, for any x, if x is a cow, then x is a mammal.

so another symbolization of 2 is: $(x)(Ox \supset Mx) \cdot (x)(Cx \supset Mx)$

Why is **(x)((Ox · Cx) ⊃ Mx)** an incorrect symbolization of **Horses and cows are mammals**?

Because ___*We have no horse-cows!*___

_____

_____

Next frame.

# 123

**Horses and cows are mammals.** should not be symbolized as **(x)((Ox ·
Cx) ⊃ Mx)** because no individual is both a horse *and* a cow. Therefore,
*instances* of **(Ox · Cx) ⊃ Mx** will never have a True antecedent. The
original sentence does *not* assert that anything which is *both* a horse
and a cow is a mammal; rather anything that is *either* a horse or cow
is a mammal.

Another example:

> Every voter is a Republican or Democrat.
> Vx: x is a voter.
> Rx: x is a Republican.
> Dx: x is a Democrat.

$$(x)(Vx) \supset (Dx \vee Rx)$$

Choose the correct symbolization.

1. (x)(Vx ⊃ Rx) ∨ Dx

2. (y)(Vy ⊃ (Ry ∨ Dy))    — *Variable chven inconseg.*

3. (x)(Vx ⊃ (Rx · Dx))    ?

Choice 1, turn to frame 124.

2, turn to frame 125.

3, turn to frame 126.

# 124

You chose **(x) (Vx ⊃ Rx) ∨ Dx** as the symbolization of **Every voter is a Republican or Democrat.** Perhaps you should review the discussion about the placement of parentheses and the scope of quantifiers in frame 120.

*Your* formula is a disjunction of two parts '(x)(Vx ⊃ Rx)' and 'Dx'. Thus we would interpret this as:

Every voter is a Republican *or* x is a Democrat.

This is not a sentence because of the *free* x. In other words, because of the placement of the parentheses, the 'x' in 'Dx' is not *bound* to the 'x' in 'Rx' by the quantifier.

Return to frame 123 and try again.

# 125

**(y)(Vy ⊃ (Ry ∨ Dy))** is the symbolization of **For any individual y, if y is a voter, then y is a Republican or y is a Democrat.** The choice of individual variable is inconsequential. If 'Vx' symbolizes: x is a voter, then 'Vy' symbolizes 'y is a voter', and 'Vz': z is a voter.

Notice that **Every voter is a Republican or Democrat.** is in fact a False sentence. It is important to see how it is falsified: by finding one substitution instance of 'Vy ⊃ (Ry ∨ Dy)' that is false. That is we locate an individual who makes the antecedent True (−whose name substituted for 'y' in 'Vy' yields a True sentence). We now have an individual who is a voter. We then discover that '(Ry ∨ Dy)' is False of that individual. More explicitly the individual voter is neither a Republican nor a Democrat. If John, a socialist, is this individual we have (j: John):

Vj ⊃ (Rj ∨ Dj)

a conditional whose *antecedent is True* but whose *consequent is False*. Hence this *conditional* is False. Since not every substitution instance is True, the universal quantification of **Vy ⊃ (Ry ∨ Dy)** is False.

Symbolize

Only the brave deserve the fair.
Bx: x is brave.
Dx: x deserves the fair.

Go to frame 127.

150

# 126

(x)(Vx ⊃ (Rx · Dx)) symbolizes **For any x, if x is a voter  then x is BOTH a Republican AND a Democrat.**

We want our voter to be either one or the other.

Return to frame 123
and try again.

# 127

**(x)(Dx ⊃ Bx)** or **(x)(~Bx ⊃~Dx)** symbolizes **Only the brave deserve the fair.**

We must be clear on the paraphrase step. We are not claiming

For *any* x, if x is brave, then x deserves the fair.

for this means *every brave person deserves the fair.* We *are* claiming, on the other hand,

For any x, x deserves the fair *only if* x is brave.

That is, either of the two:

For any x, if x *does* deserve the fair then x is brave.
For any x, if x is not brave then x does not deserve the fair.

Example:
Some who read the book are not pleased.
Rx: x reads the book.
Px: x is pleased.

(There is at least one x such that x reads the book and x is *not* pleased.)

Choose the correct symbolization:

1. (∃x)(Rx ·~Px)

2. (x)(Rx ⊃~Px)

_____

1. (∃x)(Rx ·~Px)
2. is a symbolization of **Everyone who reads the book is not pleased.**

Next frame.

# 128

Circle the formula that correctly symbolizes the given English sentence.

All those who are wealthy or who own land are opposed to the plan if they are not stupid.
   Wx: x is wealthy.
   Ox: x owns land.
   Px: x is opposed to the plan.
   Sx: x is stupid.

1. $(x)((Wx \lor Ox \cdot \sim Sx) \supset Px)$

2. $(\exists x)((Wx \lor Ox) \supset (\sim Sx \cdot Px))$

3. $(x)((Wx \lor Ox) \supset (Px \supset \sim Sx))$

4. $(x)((Wx \lor Ox) \supset (\sim Sx \supset Px))$

---

4. $(x)((Wx \lor Ox) \supset (\sim Sx \supset Px))$

---

A kiwi is a rare bird.
   Kx: x is a kiwi.
   Rx: x is rare.
   Bx: x is a bird.

1. $(\exists x)(Kx \cdot Rx \cdot Bx)$

2. $(x)(Kx \supset (Rx \cdot Bx))$

3. $(x)((Rx \cdot Bx) \supset Kx)$

4. $(\exists x)(Kx \supset (Rx \cdot Bx))$

---

2. $(x)(Kx \supset (Rx \cdot Bx))$

Next frame.

153

# 129

Circle a reasonable English interpretation of the given formula.

(x)((Sx ·~Tx) ⊃ Ox)
    Sx: x is a society.
    Tx: x is totalitarian.
    Ox: x is tolerable.

1. Any totalitarian society is intolerable.

2. Every tolerable society is not totalitarian.

3. A society that is not totalitarian is tolerable.

4. No tolerable society is totalitarian.

---

3. A society that is not totalitarian is tolerable.

---

~(∃y)(Oy · My · Ly)
    Oy: y is oviparous.
    My: y is a mammal.
    Ly: y can fly.

1. There is no oviparous mammal that can fly.

2. It is not the case that all mammals that can fly are oviparous.

3. Some oviparous mammals cannot fly.

---

1. There is no oviparous mammal that can fly.

Page 155.

TEAR THIS SHEET OUT

Individual constants: a, b, c, . . ., m
Individual variables: u, v, w, x, y, z
Predicates: A, B, C, D, E, I, J, . . ., Z
All F's are G's: (x)(Fx ⊃ Gx)
Some F's are G's: (∃x)(Fx · Gx)

------------------------------------ FOLD HERE ------------------------------------

# 130

How are you doing?

1. '_____ has a headache.' is a:
   A. name
   B. predicate
   C. sentence
   D. quantifier

   _____ *B.*

2. Names of individuals are abbreviated by (capital/small) letters.

3. Predicate letters followed by the appropriate number of individual variables are *abbreviations* of

   *help* _sentential functions_

4. A universally quantified sentence is false if _There is one instance of falsehood_

5. A sentence of the form **Some M are not S** is symbolized:
   A. (x)(Mx ⊃ ~Sx)
   B. (∃x)(Mx ⊃ ~Sx)
   C. (x)(Mx · ~Sx)
   D. (∃x)(Mx · ~Sx)

   _____ *D*

   $\exists x(Mx \cdot \sim Sx)$

---

1. B
2. small
3. sentential functions

4. One substitution instance of the sentential function is false
5. D

Next frame.

# 131

Suppose ~(∃x)Fx, which can be read

(1) It is not the case that for some x, Fx.
(2) There is not even one x such that Fx.
(3) There is no x such that Fx.

Under this supposition, is (∃x)Fx True or False?

Since (∃x)Fx is *False*, by the truth conditions for an existentially quantified sentence, every substitution instance of Fx is False.

What, now, is the truth value of *every* substitution instance of ~Fx?

True / False

---

True, since if p is False, ~p is True.

---

If *every* substitution instance of ~Fx is True, then (x)~Fx is True. Hence,

If ~(∃x)Fx then   .

---

If ~(∃x)Fx then (x)~Fx.

Next frame.

# 132

Let us assume that (x)~Fx is True.

(1) Every substitution instance of ~Fx is (True/False).
(2) If every instance of ~Fx is *True*, every instance of Fx is (True/False).
(3) If every instance of Fx is *False*, then there is no instance of Fx which is True.

What then is the truth value of ~(∃x)Fx? (True/False)

---

True

---

You have just followed the argument to show:

If (x)~Fx then ~(∃x)Fx

We argued earlier that

If ~(∃x)Fx then (x)~Fx

Thus we have discovered the *logical equivalence* between

(x)~Fx       and       ~(∃x)Fx

Consider now a different sentence. What do we claim when we assert:       ~(x)Fx?

1. Nothing satisfies the predicate F.

2. Not everything satisfies the predicate F.

Choice 1, turn to frame 133.

Choice 2, turn to frame 134.

159

# 133

~(x)Fx is the denial of (x)Fx.

(x)Fx claims: Every individual x is such that Fx. To deny this is to claim: *Not every* individual x is such that Fx. This is *not* to say: *No* individual x is such that Fx.

For example, if I deny **Everything is blue.**, I am not claiming **Nothing is blue.** All I am claiming is that not all things in the universe are blue.

Next frame.

# 134

~(x)Fx claims that *not every* individual x is such that Fx.

But if not every individual x is such that Fx, not every substitution instance of Fx is True, so at least one instance of Fx is *False*.

And if p is False then ~p is True, so *that* individual which does *not* satisfy F *does* satisfy ~F. In other words, instances of ~Fx are True where those instances of Fx are False, and furthermore some instance of Fx *is* False.

Concretely, if not everything is blue, then some (at least one) thing is non-blue. That is,

    If ~(x)Bx      then      (∃x)~Bx

There is in fact a logical equivalence between sentences of these forms:

    ~(x)Fx      and      (∃x)~Fx.

Our previously discovered logical equivalence was between
    (x)~Fx      and

1. (∃x)~Fx

2. ~(x)Fx

3. ~(∃x)Fx

4. ~(∃x)~Fx

(Hint: Read these aloud in English.)

    3.

---

3. ~(∃x)Fx (See frame 132.)

Next frame.

# 135

(∃x)~Fx is logically equivalent to ~(x)Fx
(x)~Fx is logically equivalent to ~(∃x)Fx

A simple way to remember these equivalences is in the form of a mechanical transformation rule.

*NB*

*One can move a negation sign through a quantifier (from right to left, or left to right) by changing the quantity of the quantifier to obtain a logically equivalent sentence.*

According to this rule,

(x)~~Fx is equivalent to ~(∃x)~Fx

and ~(∃x)~Fx is equivalent to ~~(x)Fx

Also (∃x)~~Fx is equivalent to ~(x)~Fx

and ~(x)~Fx is equivalent to ~~(∃x)Fx

If p is logically equivalent to q, and q is equivalent to r, is p equivalent to r?

*p = q*
*q = r*
*p = r   yes*

Yes. Turn to frame 136.

No.  Turn to frame 137.

# 136

p and r are logically equivalent.

If, Exy: x is logically equivalent to y, then, for any sentences p,q, r:

$$(Epq \ \& \ Eqr) \supset Epr$$

This transitivity of logical equivalence plus our rule for moving nega-tion signs through quantifiers by *changing* the quantity, allows us to discover a great many logical equivalences.

> (∃x)~~Fx  is equivalent to  ~(x)~Fx
> ~(x)~Fx   is equivalent to  ~~(∃x)Fx

and from Part I, the double negation of any sentence is logically equiva-lent to the original sentence, hence ~~(∃x)Fx is logically equivalent to (∃x)Fx.

Circle the formula below that is logically equivalent to ~(∃x)~Fx.

1. (x)Fx

2. ~~(∃x)Fx

3. (∃x)Fx

Choice 1, turn to frame 138.

2, turn to frame 139.

3, turn to frame 140.

# 137

If p is logically equivalent to q, p is True (False) under precisely the same conditions as q.

And if q is logically equivalent to r, q is True (False) under precisely the same conditions as r.

Hence, p, q and r are True (False) under precisely the same conditions.

Therefore, p and r are True (False) under precisely the same conditions and so p and r *are logically equivalent.*

Turn back to frame 136.

# 138

Correct. ~(∃x)~Fx is equivalent to ~~(x)Fx which in turn is equivalent to (x)Fx.

Remember that this discussion is on a level of complete generality. 'F' has been used as a *predicate* variable ranging over any predicate no matter how complex. This degree of abstraction has prevented the actual structure of the predicate from confusing us.

Now let us look at the structure of the sentential function following the quantifiers.

> **Some men are tall.** is logically equivalent to **Some tall things are men.**

Symbolically, **(∃x)(Mx · Tx)** is logically equivalent to **(∃x)(Tx · Mx)**
(∃x)(Fx ∨ Gx) is logically equivalent to which of these?

1. (∃x)(Fx · Gx)

2. (∃x)(Gx ∨ Fx)

2

Choice 1, turn to frame 141.

Choice 2, turn to frame 142.

# 139

No. You moved the second negation sign in $\sim(\exists x)\sim Fx$ through the quantifier to the left, but you did not *change the quantity* of the quantifier.

Return to frame 136 and try again.

# 140

No. A double negation consists of two negation signs *side by side.* There is *no* double negation in ~(∃x)~Fx.

Hint: Move the second negation sign to the left *through the quantifier.* Then you will have a double negation.

Return to frame 136 and try again.

# 141

Wrong. For example, say the variable 'x' ranges over individual numbers, and (∃x)(Fx ∨ Gx) is, for instance, **Some numbers are even or odd.** or **(∃x)(Ex ∨ Ox).**

But **(∃x)(Ex · Ox)** would symbolize **Some numbers are even AND odd.**

Next frame.

# 142

($\exists$x)(Fx $\lor$ Gx) is logically equivalent to ($\exists$x)(Gx $\lor$ Fx). And all the following pairs are logically equivalent *except one.*

1. (x)~~Fx                         (x)Fx

2. ($\exists$x)~(Fx $\cdot$ Gx)              ($\exists$x)(~Fx $\lor$ ~Gx)

3. (x)(Fx $\supset$ Gx)      *No !*     (x)(Gx $\supset$ Fx)

4. (y)(Fy $\equiv$ Gy)                  (y)(Gy $\equiv$ Fy)

Which pair is not logically equivalent? _____3_____

---

3. (x)(Fx $\supset$ Gx) is *not* logically equivalent to (x)(Gx $\supset$ Fx), since p $\supset$ q is not equivalent to q $\supset$ p.
   The others can easily be checked by truth tables.

| | | |
|---|---|---|
| ~~p | p | (Double Negation) |
| ~(p $\cdot$ q) | (~p $\lor$ ~q) | (De Morgan's Law) |
| (p $\equiv$ q) | (q $\equiv$ p) | |

Next frame.

# 143

*The logical form of a sentential function is the logical form of a sentence that results from that sentential function when names (individual constants) replace the variables.*

If we want to exhibit the logical form of

    (1)  Ax ⊃ (By ∨ Cxy)

we replace the variables by individual constants

    (2)  Ak ⊃ (Bf ∨ Ckf)

   Now 2 is a compound sentence consisting of the three *simple* sentences **Ak, Bf,** and **Ckf**. The logical form of 1 is:

    p ⊃ (q ∨ r)

because the logical form of a compound, non-quantified sentence is found by replacing the simple sentences by sentential variables p, q, r, etc.

   This is just a tedious method for recognizing that

    (Ax · Bz) ⊃~Dyy

has the same logical form as which one of these?

1. (Dxy · Az) ⊃~Ay
2. (Bx · By) ⊃~By

---

1 is correct. The logical form of 2 is given by: (p · q) ⊃~q.

Next frame.

# 144

*Two sentential functions are logically equivalent if sentences of their logical forms are determined (by truth tables) to be logically equivalent.*

Consider two sentential functions: (Fx ⊃ Gx) and ~(Fx ·~Gx). The logical forms of these sentential functions are:

(p ⊃ q)        and        ~(p ·~q)

Truth table analysis shows that sentences of these forms are logically equivalent. Fill in the table below.

| p | q | ~q | p ·~q | ~(p ·~q) | p ⊃ q |
|---|---|----|-------|----------|-------|
| T | T | F | F | T | T |
| T | F | T | T | F | F |
| F | T | F | F | T | T |
| F | F | T | F | T | T |

| p | q | ~q | p ·~q | ~(p ·~q) | p ⊃ q |
|---|---|----|-------|----------|-------|
| T | T | F | F | T | T |
| T | F | T | T | F | F |
| F | T | F | F | T | T |
| F | F | T | F | T | T |

Next frame.

# 145

Since *sentences* of the forms (p ⊃ q) and ~(p ·~q) are logically equivalent, so are *sentential functions* of that logical form, i.e.,

(Fx ⊃ Gx)          and          ~(Fx ·~Gx).

If, in a *quantified* sentence, we substitute a logically equivalent *sentential function* for a sentential function occurring in the original sentence, we obtain a new sentence which is logically equivalent to the original (as long as the same variables are used with the same predicates).

If we substitute ~(Fx ·~Gx) for (Fx ⊃ Gx) in (x)(Fx ⊃ Gx) we obtain (x)~(Fx ·~Gx), which is logically equivalent to (x)(Fx ⊃ Gx).

**Cows moo.** symbolized **(x)(Cx ⊃ Mx)** is logically equivalent to **(x)~(Cx ·~Mx)**. And **(x)~(Cx ·~Mx)** is logically equivalent to

1. ~(x)(Cx ·~Mx)
2. ~(∃x)(Cx ·~Mx)

*2*

Choice 1, turn to frame 146.

Choice 2, turn to frame 147.

# 146

You didn't *change the quantity* of the quantifier when you moved the negation sign to the left. Your choice $\sim$(x)(Cx $\cdot\sim$Mx) is interpreted by **Not everything is a cow and does not moo.** This is a true sentence (since not everything is a cow), but it is not equivalent to **Cows moo.**

Next frame.

# 147

**Cows moo.** is equivalent to $\sim(\exists x)(Cx \cdot \sim Mx)$, which is interpreted by
**There is no cow that does not moo.**

Often we are not interested so much in logical equivalents to a given sentence, but rather in a *contradictory* sentence. What sentence *contradicts* **Cows moo**?

There *is* a cow ___that____doesn't moo___
(Fill in.)

---

There is a cow that does not moo.

Next frame.

# 148

When we seek a contradictory formula to a *universally* quantified formula, we usually rely on one of these two logical equivalences:

(1)    ~(p ⊃ q)      (p ·~q)
(2)    ~(p ⊃~q)    (p · q)

Denying:        (x)(Cx ⊃ Mx)      (Cows moo.)
we obtain:    ~(x)(Cx ⊃ Mx)    (Not all cows moo.)

Moving the negation sign to the right through the quantifier yields:

(∃x)~(Cx ⊃ Mx)        (There is something such that it is not the case if it is a cow then it moos.)

Now, using 1, we get: (∃x)(Cx ·~Mx)     (There is a cow who does not moo.)

2 would be used in working with a sentence such as:

No pig swims.         (x)(Px ⊃~Sx)
Denying this gives:    ~(x)(Px ⊃~Sx)

What is the final formula we obtain, using 2?
1. (∃x)(Px · Sx)
2. (x)(Px · Sx)

Choice 1, turn to frame 149.

Choice 2, turn to frame 150.

# 149

Correct.    $\sim(x)(Px \supset \sim Sx)$
            $(\exists x)\sim(Px \supset \sim Sx)$
and by 2    $(\exists x)(Px \cdot Sx)$

This formula is interpreted by **Some pigs swim.** which contradicts our original sentence **No pig swims.**

Turn to frame 151.

# 150

You neglected to change the quantity of the quantifier when you moved the negation sign to the right.

$$\sim(x)(Px \supset \sim Sx)$$

becomes $\quad\quad\quad (\exists x)\sim(Px \supset \sim Sx)$

and using 2, we get: $(\exists x)(Px \cdot Sx)$

which is interpreted: *Some pigs swim.* This contradicts our original sentence: *No pig swims.*

Next frame.

# 151

Let's look at a diagram:

| | |
|---|---|
| All F's are G's | No F's are G's |
| $(x)(Fx \supset Gx)$ | $(x)(Fx \supset \sim Gx)$ |

contradictories

| | |
|---|---|
| Some F's are G's | Some F's are not G's |
| $(\exists x)(Fx \cdot Gx)$ | $(\exists x)(Fx \cdot \sim Gx)$ |

The *negation* of one corner can be shown to be logically equivalent to the diagonally opposite corner.

Let's review what we have learned about logical equivalences and about contradictories, before moving on to new material.

If we have a quantified sentence with a negation sign on either side

of the quantifier, we can move the negation sign _to the_ _through the other quantifier_ _side of_ & _changing_ _the quantity_ of _the quantifier_

and obtain a logically equivalent sentence. (Fill in the blanks.)

---

We can move the negation sign *through the quantifier changing the quantity of the quantifier* and obtain a logically equivalent sentence.

Next frame.

# 152

If two sentential functions are logically equivalent, we can _____

*substitute ~~the~~ one in for the other*

in a quantified sentence and obtain a logically equivalent sentence (if there is no change in the variables).

---

We can *substitute one for the other* in a quantified sentence and obtain a logically equivalent sentence.

Next frame.

# 153

If two sentences are logically equivalent, the negation of one

_is the contradicts to_ the other.

---

contradicts; is contradictory to

# 154

A. Write the English sentence which contradicts the sentence below.
   No politician is both honest and rich.

*There Some politicians are both honest & rich*

---

Some politicians are both honest and rich.

---

B. Which *two* of the following symbolize the English sentence:
   No politician is both honest and rich.
   Px: x is a politician.
   Ox: x is honest.
   Rx: x is rich.

1. ~(x)(Px ⊃ (Ox · Rx))
2. (x)((Px · ~Ox) ⊃ Rx)
3. (x)(Px ⊃ (~Ox ∨ ~Rx))
4. (∃x)~(Px · (Ox · Rx))
5. ~(∃x)(Px · (Ox · Rx))
6. (x)(Px ⊃ (~Ox · ~Rx))

(Note:  ~(p · q), (~p ∨ ~q), (p ⊃ ~q) are equivalent formulae.)

---

3. (x)(Px ⊃ (~Ox ∨ ~Rx))
5. ~(∃x)(Px · (Ox · Rx))

If you are incorrect, go to the next frame.

If you are correct, turn to frame 156.

# 155

Part A is really commonsensical. If you were to argue against the truth of **No politician is both honest and rich** you would point to some (at least one) politician who *was* both honest and rich.

Part B is more difficult. There are several ways to get at this problem. The easiest, I think, is to *deny the denial.* That is, deny **There is a politician who is both honest and rich.**

$\sim(\exists x)(Px \cdot (Ox \cdot Rx))$      (choice 5)

This is logically equivalent to each of the following:

$(x)\sim(Px \cdot (Ox \cdot Rx))$         $\sim(p \cdot q)$

$(x)(Px \supset \sim(Ox \cdot Rx))$        $(p \supset \sim q)$

$(x)(Px \supset (\sim Ox \vee \sim Rx))$     $\sim(p \cdot q)$ goes to $(\sim p \vee \sim q)$
(choice 3)

Another way to symbolize the given sentence is to appeal to the general form:

No F's are G's: $(x)(Fx \supset \sim Gx)$

This gives immediately: $(x)(Px \supset \sim(Ox \cdot Rx))$ This sentence can be manipulated in several ways to yield numbers 3 and 5.

Next frame.

# 156

Circle the symbolizations of the English sentences:

Jx: x is a junior.
Sx: x submitted a paper.
Px: x passed the course.

Every junior who submitted a paper passed the course.

1. (x)(Jx · Sx · Px)

2. (x)(Jx ≡ (Sx · Px))

3. (x)(Jx ⊃ (Sx · Px))

4. (x)((Jx · Sx) ⊃ Px)

*(handwritten: (x)[(Jx · Sx) ⊃ Px)*

---

4. (x)((Jx · Sx) ⊃ Px)    That is: For every x, *if* x is a junior *and* x submitted a paper *then* x passed the course.

---

No junior who submitted a paper passed the course.

1. ~(x)((Jx · Sx) ⊃ Px)

2.   (x)(Jx ⊃~(Sx · Px))

3. (x)((Jx · Sx) ⊃~Px)

4. ~(x)(Jx ⊃ (Sx · Px))

*(handwritten: (x)(Jx · Sx) ⊃~Px)*

---

3. (x)((Jx · Sx) ⊃~Px) That is: For any x, *if* x is a junior who submitted a paper, *then* x did not pass the course. (OR: Every junior who submitted a paper did not pass the course.)

Next frame.

183

# 157

Consider **(x)((Jx · Sx) ⊃ Px)** and **(x)((Jx · Sx) ⊃~Px)**
Circle which of the following applies:

1. Logically equivalent

2. Contradictory

3. Neither

Choice 1, turn to frame 158.

2, turn to frame 159.

3, turn to frame 160.

# 158

Wrong. **(x)((Jx · Sx) ⊃ Px)** and **(x)((Jx · Sx) ⊃~Px)** can't be True (False) under precisely the same conditions. Let us consider a situation where these two do not have the same truth value.

Suppose we found an individual, say d, who satisfied **(Jx · Sx)**. That is, suppose d were a junior who submitted a paper. Now either Pd or ~Pd. That is to say, either d passed the course or he didn't.

In one case, **(Jd · Sd) ⊃ Pd** is True, and **(Jd · Sd) ⊃~Pd** False, and in the other case, the truth values of these sentences (substitution instances of **(Jx · Sx) ⊃ Px** and **(Jx · Sx) ⊃ ~ Px)**) are reversed.

Return to frame 157 and choose another answer.

# 159

Not quite. If **(x)((Jx · Sx) ⊃ Px)** is False, it does not follow that **(x)((Jx · Sx) ⊃ ~Px)** is True.

In English, if **All juniors who submitted a paper passed the course.** is False, it does not mean that no juniors who submitted a paper passed the course. After all, some of those juniors may have passed, and some may not have passed.

Return to frame 157 and choose the correct answer.

# 160

Correct. They are clearly not logically equivalent. They are not contradictory, since the contradictory of

$(x)((Jx \cdot Sx) \supset Px)$

which is interpreted by **Every junior who submitted a paper passed the course.** is the sentence

$\sim(x)((Jx \cdot Sx) \supset Px)$

which is interpreted by **Not every junior who submitted a paper passed the course.**

Our original formulae are of the forms:

All A are B        and        No A are B.

and these are neither equivalent nor contradictory.

After all this abstract material you might want to take a rest. Here is a good place to stop and mull over the concepts of logical equivalence and contradiction.

When you return to this program you might wish to review the material in this section. If so, begin with frame 131 and run through this part of the program again. It should not take as long the second time through.

The program continues in the next frame.

# 161

Would you like to test yourself to see if you have a firm grasp on the material in the previous section? Circle the correct choice.

1. No G is H [(symbolized: (x)(Gx ⊃ ~Hx)] is contradictory to:

(a) All G is H            (x)(Gx ⊃ Hx)

(b) Some G is H        (∃x)(Gx · Hx)

(c) Some G is not H     (∃x)(Gx ·~Hx)

2. ~(∃x)~~Fx is logically equivalent to

(a) (x)~Fx            ~(∃ν) Fx

(b) (∃x)~Fx

(c) ~(x)Fx

3. **If every senior at the party was not drunk, then some freshmen were happy.** should be symbolized:
       Sx: x is a senior
       Px: x was at the party
       Dx: x was drunk
       Ry: y is a freshman
       Ay: y is happy

(a) (x)(y)((Sx · Px ·~Dx · Ry) ⊃ Ay)

(b) (x)(Sx · Px ·~Dx) ⊃ (y)(Ry ⊃ Ay)

(c) (x)(Sx · Px ·~Dx) ⊃ (∃y)(Ry ⊃ Ay) .

(d) (x)((Sx · Px) ⊃~Dx) ⊃ (∃y)(Ry · Ay)

4. Suppose you know that two *sentential functions* Fx and Gx are logically equivalent. What is the relation between
        ~(x)Fx      and      (∃x)~Gx?

(a) logically equivalent           Fx · ≠ Gx
                                     ~x) F

(b) contradictory

(c) neither

---

1. b                            3. d
2. a                            4. a

Next frame.

# 162

When faced with the problem of determining if two symbolic formulae are logically equivalent, how would you begin?

A. I would begin by moving negation signs through the quantifiers of one of the formulae.

B. I would begin by replacing the sentential functions following the quantifiers by some logically equivalent sentential functions.

C. I do not want to commit myself ahead of time. I would begin as in A or B depending on the formulae in question.

---

Some people adopt a standard procedure for all problems, and always try one attack first. Choices A and B are not incorrect, but the flexibility in approach C has much to be said for it. There is no right way to begin since there is no *general* procedure for determining when two formulae are logically equivalent.

Next frame.

# 163

There are many more techniques for proving that two formulae are logically equivalent besides playing around with negation signs or substituting sentential functions whose equivalence can be determined by truth functional analysis. You should, if you are interested, consult some other text for these proof procedures.

The following fact may be of passing interest to you:

> If two formulae are logically equivalent then it is possible to construct a proof showing that they are.

(The statement just made is itself provably true.)

Do you suppose that there is a *general* method for showing that two formulae are contradictory?

Yes/No

Yes. Turn to frame 164.

No. Turn to frame 165.

# 164

No, there is not.

If there were a general method for determining contradictories, there would be then a general method for determining logical equivalences.

Do you see why this would be so? Think about it a moment and then turn to the next frame to see a fuller explanation.

# 165

There cannot be a general procedure for determining contradictories (GPC).

I have already stated (but not proved) that there is no general procedure for determining logical equivalence (GPLE). And if there were a GPC then there would be a GPLE.

If p and q are logically equivalent, then p and ~q are contradictory, and conversely. Our GPLE would be this:

To determine if p and q are logically equivalent, use GPC on p and ~q to determine if they are contradictory. If they are, then p and q are logically equivalent.

Show the following formulae are contradictory:

1. (∃x)(Ax ∨ Bx ∨ Cx)    → ~(x)~(~Ax ⊃ (Bx ∨ Cx))

2. (x)~(~Ax ⊃ (Bx ∨ Cx))    (∃x)(~Ax ⊃ (Bx ∨ Cx))

A·x ∨ (Bx ∨ C)
Ax ∨ Bx ∨ Cx

---

There are several correct ways of doing this, of course. I found the simplest procedure to be to show that 1 is logically equivalent to the denial of 2. The denial of 2 is:      ~(x)~(~Ax ⊃ (Bx ∨ Cx))
What was my next step?

# 166

1.           (∃x)(Ax ∨ Bx ∨ Cx)

Denial of 2. ~(x)~(~Ax ⊃ (Bx ∨ Cx))

My next step is either to replace '~(x)~' by '(∃x)' or, to move the second negation sign one place to the left,

    2a:      ~~( ∃x)(~Ax ⊃ (Bx ∨ Cx))

and then by double negation:

    2b:      (∃x)(~Ax ⊃ (Bx ∨ Cx))

Now all I have to do is show the sentential functions following '(∃x)' in 1 and 2b are equivalent. We can insert parentheses in 1 any way we please, and so we find that we must show the logical equivalence between:

    (Ax ∨ (Bx ∨ Cx))
    (~Ax ⊃ (Bx ∨ Cx))

I could set up truth tables to show the logical equivalence between

    (p ∨ (q ∨ r))        and        (~p ⊃ (q ∨ r))

but do you see a further simplification of the problem?

Next frame.

# 167

Since '(Bx ∨ Cx)' occurs in both sentential functions as a unit, I could determine the equivalence between

$$(p \lor q) \qquad \text{and} \qquad (\sim p \supset q)$$

Since p and q are variables for any sentence (sentential function), I could let p be **Ax** and q be **(Bx ∨ Cx).**

In any event, we show by truth table analysis the equivalence between:

| | | | |
|---|---|---|---|
| | (p ∨ (q ∨ r)) | and | (~p ⊃ (q ∨ r)) |
| or | (p ∨ q) | and | (~p ⊃ q) |

*Do it!*

This tells us that **(Ax ∨ (Bx ∨ Cx))** and **(~Ax ⊃ (Bx ∨ Cx))** are logically equivalent. And thus, so are:

$$(\exists x)(Ax \lor (Bx \lor Cx)) \qquad \text{and} \qquad (\exists x)(\sim Ax \supset (Bx \lor Cx))$$

But the right hand formula is equivalent to: ~(x)~(~Ax ⊃ (Bx ∨ Cx)), which is the *negation* of our original formula **(x)~(~Ax ⊃ (Bx ∨ Cx))**

Since one formula is equivalent to the negation of the other, the original formulae are contradictory.

Next frame.

# 168

Are the following two formulae logically equivalent?

1. (x)(Ax ⊃ Bx) ⊃ (∃y)Cy
2. (∃y)Cy ∨ (∃x)(Ax ·~Bx)

Yes/No

(∃x) ~[(Ax ⊃ Bx) ⊃ ∃y (Cy )

(y) ~[ Cy ∨ (∃x)( Ax · ~Bx)

(∃x) (Ax · ~Bx ) ∨ (∃y) Cy

~(∃x) ~(Ax · ~Bx)

~ (∃x) (~Ax ∨ Bx )

~ (∃x) (Ax ⊃ Bx) ∨ (∃y) Cy

(x) ~(Ax ⊃ Bx) ∨ (∃y) Cy

(x) (Ax ⊃ Bx) ⊃ (∃y Cy

Yes. Turn to frame 169.

No. Turn to frame 170.

195

# 169

Correct. If you just *guessed* go on to the next frame where it is worked out in detail.

If you really worked out this difficult problem, you have my congratulations, and you may turn to frame 171.

# 170

1. $(x)(Ax \supset Bx) \supset (\exists y)Cy$
2. $(\exists y)Cy \lor (\exists x)(Ax \cdot \sim Bx)$

These are logically equivalent.

First of all, $(p \lor q)$ is equivalent to $(q \lor p)$, so switch 2 to:

2a.     $(\exists x)(Ax \cdot \sim Bx) \lor (\exists y)Cy$

Now you just worked out a truth table showing that $(\sim p \supset q)$ and $(p \lor q)$ are equivalent, so 2a is equivalent to:

2b.     $\sim (\exists x)(Ax \cdot \sim Bx) \supset (\exists y)Cy$

All you have to do now is show the *antecedents* of 1 and 2b to be equivalent. That is, show

$(x)(Ax \supset Bx)$     and     $\sim (\exists x)(Ax \cdot \sim Bx)$

to be equivalent. Move the negation sign to the right obtaining:

$(x)\sim (Ax \cdot \sim Bx)$

Now show that $(p \supset q)$ is equivalent to $\sim (p \cdot \sim q)$ by truth tables, and you are finished.

$$\exists x(Ax \cdot \sim Bx) \lor (\exists y)Cy$$

$$\sim (\exists x)(Ax \cdot \sim Bx) \supset (\exists y)Cy$$

$$(x) \sim (Ax \cdot Bx)$$

$$(x) \sim Ax \lor \sim\sim Bx$$

$$(x) \sim Ax \lor Bx$$

$$Bx \lor \sim Ax$$

Next frame.

# 171

Match the symbolization with its appropriate English sentence. (Take the universe restricted to people only.)

1. (x)Ljx      __c__      a. John likes someone.
2. (∃x)Lxj      __d__      b. Everyone likes John.
3. (x)Lxj      __b__      c. John likes everyone.
4. (∃x)Ljx      __a__      d. Someone likes John.

---

1. (x)Ljx      c. John likes everyone.
2. (∃x)Lxj      d. Someone likes John.
3. (x)Lxj      b. Everyone likes John.
4. (∃x)Ljx      a. John likes someone.

Next frame.

# 172

1. **(∃x)Ljx** symbolizes: John likes someone.
   **(∃y)(∃x)Lyx** symbolizes: Someone likes someone.

2. **(x)Ljx** symbolizes: John likes everyone.
   **(y)(x)Lyx** symbolizes: _Everyone likes everyone_
   (Fill in blank.)

---

**(y)(x)Lyx** symbolizes: Everyone likes everyone.

# 173

1. **(∃x)(y)Lxy** can be expanded partially to read:
   (a) There is *some* x such that for *any* y, that x likes y. THAT IS:
   (b) Someone likes everyone.

2. **(∃y)(x)Lxy,** when the quantifiers are stated in English, becomes:
   (a) There is *some* y such that for *any* x, x likes that y. THAT IS:
   (b) There is someone whom everyone likes.

3. **(x)(∃y)Lxy** is to be read:

   (a) *Everyone likes someone*    such that x
                                            likes that y

   (Fill in like lines (a) in the above examples.)

---

For *any* x, there is *some* y, such that x likes that y.

---

Circle the English sentence below which interprets formula 3.

Someone *is liked by* everyone.

~~Everyone *likes* someone.~~

---

Everyone *likes* someone (or other).

Notice the difference between the formulae 2 and 3, and notice how the interpretations of 2 and 3 differ in meaning.

Next frame.

# 174

1. John likes everyone who studies philosophy.
   (a) For any x, if x studies philosophy then John likes x.
   (b) (x)(Sx ⊃ Ljx)

2. John likes only those who study philosophy.
   (a) For any x, John likes x *only if* x studies philosophy.

Circle the correct symbolization of 2a.

(x)(Ljx ⊃ Sx)

(x)(Sx ⊃ Ljx)

(x)(~Sx ⊃ Ljx)

---

(x)(Ljx ⊃ Sx)

(x)(Sx ⊃ Ljx) is the symbolization of 1.

Next frame.

# 175

**(x)(Sx ⊃ Ljx)** symbolizes **John likes anyone who studies philosophy.**

What does '(∃y)(x)(Sx ⊃ Lyx)' symbolize?

1. John likes someone who studies philosophy.
2. Everyone likes someone who studies philosophy.
3. Someone likes anyone who studies philosophy.

3

---

3. Someone likes anyone who studies philosophy.

Next frame.

# 176

1. John likes no one who studies philosophy.
    (a) For anyone who studies philosophy, John does not like him.
    (b) For any x, if Sx, then ~Ljx
    (c) (x)(Sx ⊃ ~Ljx)

2. John likes no one who hits his (John's) sister.
    Sxy: x is a sister of y.     (Remember: Syx: y is a sister of x.)
    Ixy: x hits y.

    (a) For any x, if *x hits a sister of John*, then John does not like x.
        (i) x hits a sister of John.
        (ii) There is a y, x hits y and y is a sister of John.
    (b) For any x, if (∃y)(Ixy · Syj), then John does not like x.
    (c) (x)((∃y)(Ixy · Syj) ⊃ ~Ljx)

3. No one likes anyone who hits his sister. (That is, everyone is similar to John in 2 above.)
    (a) For every x and every y, if y hits a sister of x, x does not like y.
        (i) y hits a sister of x.
        (ii) There is a z, y hits z and z is a sister of x.

    (b) For every x and y, if ___(x)(y) (∃z)(Iyz · Szx)___

        then   ___x doesn't like y)___.

    (c) (x) (y) (∃z) (Iyz · Szx) ⊃ ~Lxy)

---

    (b) For every x and y, if (∃z)(Iyz · Szx), then x does not like y.
    (c) (x)(y)((∃z)(Iyz · Szx ) ⊃ ~Lxy)

Next frame.

# 177

You must watch your parentheses in problems of this sort. When we have a sentence of the form,

> For all x, if there is a y, Fy, then Gx

the existential quantifier of 'y' is in the antecedent of the (conditional) sentential function:

> if there is a y, Fy, then Gx

Let us see what the difference is between

> (∃y)Fy ⊃ p

and

> (∃y)(Fy ⊃ p)

Take: *If someone squeals, the cause is lost.*
> (a) If (∃y)Sy, then C
> (b) (∃y)Sy ⊃ C

But suppose we write: (∃y)(Sy ⊃ C). This is a True sentence if there is one name which substituted for 'y' in **(Sy ⊃ C)** yields a True sentence. Let us consider Fido, f, who is *not* a squealer. Then **(Sf ⊃ C)** is a True sentence because the antecedent **Sf** is False. The name of any non-squealer in the universe put in place of 'y' gives a True sentence.

In other words, (∃y)(Fy ⊃ p) is True if (Fy ⊃ p) is True for *some* choice of y. And any choice of y for which Fy is False will make (Fy ⊃ p) True.

On the other hand, (∃y)Fy ⊃ p is a False sentence in those cases (and only those cases) where (∃y)Fy is a True sentence and p is a False one.

Next frame.

# 178

No one likes anyone who hits his own sister.

  Lxy: x likes y

  (a) No x likes any y if y hits his own sister.

   (i)  y hits his own sister.
   (ii) (∃z)(Iyz · Szy)

  (b) For any x and any y, if _(∃z)Iyz · Szy_ then _~Lxy_

  (c) _[(x)(y)](∃z)Iyz ⊃ (x) ~Lxy_
      (Symbolize completely.)

*[handwritten annotations: "No one likes y", "No", "No", "(x)(y)(∃z)(Iyz·Szy) ⊃ ~Lxy"]*

---

(b) For any x and any y, if (∃z)(Izy · Szy) then ~Lxy
(c) (x)(y)((∃z)(Iyz · Szy) ⊃ ~Lxy)

Next frame.

# 179

In symbolizing, we paraphrase, making subject terms explicit. We then symbolize the shorter complex clauses inside the sentence and then work out to the whole sentence.

> There is a book that is read by every student who reads any book at all.
>
> > Bx: x is a book.
> > Sx: x is a student.
> > Rxy: x reads y.

Paraphrase Step:

> There is some x such that (x is a book *and* every y who is a student and who has read any book at all reads x).

Symbolize: y has read any book at all (i.e., y has read some book or other)

> $(\exists z)(Ryz \cdot Bz)$     (or equally correct: $(\exists z)(Bz \cdot Ryz)$)

Paraphrase with partial symbolization:

> $(\exists x)(x$ is a book $\cdot$ every y who is a student and $(\exists z)(Ryz \cdot Bz)$ reads x)

Symbolize now: every y who is a student reads x.

$$\underline{(y)(Sy \supset Ryx)}$$

---

$(y)(Sy \supset Ryx)$

Next frame.

# 180

Given that **Every y who is a student reads x** is symbolized: (y)(Sy ⊃ Ryx), the symbolization of **Every y who is a student and (∃z)(Ryz · Bz) reads x** is:

(y)[(Sy · (∃z)(Ryz · Bz)) ⊃ Ryx]

Note: Square brackets '[     ]' will sometimes replace parentheses for clarity and ease of reading.

Now symbolize:

There is an x such that ((x is a book) *and* (every student who reads any book at all reads x)).

(∃x) $\underline{[Bx \cdot (y)(Sy \cdot (\exists z)(Ryz \cdot Bz)) \supset Rxy}$

---

(∃x)[Bx · (y)((Sy · (∃z)(Ryz · Bz)) ⊃ Ryx)]

Next frame.

# 181

We have seen that the standard symbolic form for sentences such as:

>    All F's are G's.

is:   $(x)(Fx \supset Gx)$

1. All seniors are eligible.
   $(x)(Sx \supset Ex)$

If we restrict those F's that are G's by adding a further condition, H, (All those F's that are H's are G's) we obtain the standard form:

>    $(x)((Fx \cdot Hx) \supset Gx)$

2. Those seniors who have had chemistry are eligible.
   $(x)((Sx \cdot Cx) \supset Ex)$

This sample sentence is clearly a different assertion from:

3. All those who are eligible are seniors who have had chemistry.
   $(x)(Ex \supset (Sx \cdot Cx))$

which can also be stated in English as:
*Only* seniors who have had chemistry are eligible.

A universally quantified formula does not assert (although it may presuppose) the existence of anything. In the above examples, every one of the sentences could be as a matter of fact True, and yet there may not, in fact, *exist* one eligible person.

Existentially quantified formulae, on the other hand, do assert the existence of at least one thing satisfying one condition, or *conjointly* more than one condition.

(1) Some seniors are eligible.      $(\exists x)(Sx \cdot Ex)$
(2) Some seniors who have had chemistry are eligible.
    $(\exists x)((Sx \cdot Cx) \cdot Ex)$ This makes the same existence claim as:
(3) Some seniors who are eligible have had chemistry.
    $(\exists x)((Sx \cdot Ex) \cdot Cx)$

Next frame.

# 182

1. Gold Dollar is the favorite horse.

'Gold Dollar' is a name of some individual horse, and so will be abbreviated by an individual constant, say, 'g'. We might be tempted to say that 1 asserts that g has the property of being the favorite horse, and thus symbolize our sentence this way: Ag
But look at

2. The favorite horse is the crowd's choice.

Here 'the favorite horse' is a denoting expression referring to an individual. Shall we abbreviate this expression as 'f' and sentence 2 as: Cf? This will hardly do since from 1 and 2 we *should* be able to infer

3. Gold Dollar is the crowd's choice.

and we see no relation between 'Ag' and 'Cf' that permits this (symbolized: Cg).

Sentence 1 really asserts that the individual, Gold Dollar, is

_Identical_____ the individual, the favorite horse.
(Fill in the relationship.)

---

identical to (or: the same as)

Next frame.

# 183

Logicians use the familiar "equals" sign to symbolize the relation of *identity.*

Thus,

1. Gold Dollar is the favorite horse.
      g                  f

2. The favorite horse is the crowd's choice.
           f                  c

3. Gold Dollar is the crowd's choice.

will be symbolized:

1. $g = f$

2. $f = c$

3. $\underline{g = c}$
   (Fill in.)

---

3. $g = c$

Next frame.

x

x

x

# 184

Using the symbol for identity, we can now symbolize such sentences as:

1. Whoever is *the* winner receives ten dollars.

    i: the winner.
    Rx: x receives ten dollars.

    (a) For any x, if x is the winner, x receives ten dollars.
    (b) $(x)((x = i) \supset Rx)$

2. No more than one freshman is eligible.

    (a) If there are two freshmen who are eligible they are *not distinct* individuals.
    (b) $(x)(y)[(Fx \cdot Fy \cdot Ex \cdot Ey) \supset (x = y)]$

3. Every member of the class *except Mary* passed.

    Cx: x is a member of the class.
    Px: x passed.
    m: Mary.

    (a) For any x, if x is a member of the class and x is not Mary, then x passed.

    (b) <u>$(x)((Cx \cdot \sim(x = m) \supset Px)$</u>
    (Complete the symbolization.)

---

$(x)((Cx \cdot \sim(x = m)) \supset Px)$     or, of course,     $(x)((Cx \cdot \sim(m = x)) \supset Px)$

Next frame.

# 185

Let's look at some "real life" cases. First, an example from elementary geometry.

> (1) If any two lines are perpendicular to a third line, then they are parallel to each other.
>
> (2) If any line is perpendicular to another line, then that other line is perpendicular to the first.

Thus

> (3) If any two lines are not parallel, then it is not the case that there is some third line which is perpendicular to both.

We could begin rephrasing 1 as:

> For any x and y, *if x and y are lines* and . . .

*but* notice that only *lines* are mentioned in the three sentences above. So we can restrict our universe (of discourse) to lines. That is, the range of the individual variables will be restricted to (coplanar) lines.

1. $(x)(y)(z)[(Exz \cdot Eyz) \supset (Axy \cdot Ayx)]$

2. $(x)(y)(Exy \supset Eyx)$

3. For any x and y, if x is not parallel to y, then it is not the case there exists a z such that z is perpendicular to x and z is perpendicular to y.

Circle the correct symbolization below.

(a) $(x)(y)(\sim(Axy \supset \sim(\exists z)Ezx \cdot Ezy)$

(b) $(x)(y)(\sim Axy \supset \sim(\exists z)(Ezx \cdot Ezy))$

(c) $(x)(y)(\sim Axy \supset \sim(\exists z)(Exz \cdot Eyz))$

Choice a, go to frame 186.

b, go to frame 187.

c, go to frame 188.

# 186

Incorrect. You are not watching parentheses and scope. You chose **(x)(y)~(Axy ⊃ ~(∃z)Ezx · Ezy).** The first negation sign here represents a denial of the whole sentential function **(Axy ⊃ ~(∃z)Ezx · Ezy).** Also the scope of **(∃z)** extends only to **Ezx** and does not include **Ezy.**

Schematically:       (x)(y)~(Axy ⊃ ~(∃z)Ezx · Ezy)

Return to frame 185 and select a better answer.

(x)(y)(~**Axy** ⊃ ~(∃z)(**Ezx** · **Ezy**)) symbolizes: For any x and any y, if (x is not parallel to y), then it is not the case (there exists a z such that (z is perpendicular to x and z is perpendicular to y)).

An example from philosophy,

> (1) A substance is, by definition, not limited by anything.
> (2) Any substance can be limited only by a different substance.
> (3) If any two substances are different from one another, then one limits the other and is limited by the other.

Consequently,

> (4) If any substance exists, then no substance is different from it.

Now if we treat a definition as a universally quantified sentence, we can paraphrase as follows:

1. For any x, x is a substance if and only if x is not limited by anything.

2. For any x and y, if x is a substance and y limits x then y is a substance and different from x.

3. For any x and y, if x and y are substances and x is different from y, then

_x limits y & y limits x_

---

x limits y and x is limited by y. (or: x limits y and is limited by y)

---

4. For any x, if x is a substance, then _There is no y such that y is different from it_

---

there is no y such that y is a substance and is different from x. (or equivalently: every y which is a substance is identical to x.)

Turn to frame 189.

# 188

Incorrect. The formula **(∃z)(Exz · Eyz)** is interpreted as:

There is a z such that x is perpendicular to z and y is perpendicular to z.

It is true, according to statement 2 that if z is perpendicular to x then x is perpendicular to z. But what sentence 3 *actually asserts is*:

. . . it is not the case there is a z such that z is perpendicular to x and z is perpendicular to y.

So we must, consistent with our earlier symbolizing, place the 'z' first and 'x' and 'y' last.

The correct symbolization is:     $(x)(y)(\sim Axy \supset \sim(\exists z)(Ezx \cdot Ezy))$

Turn back to frame 187.

# 189

(1) For any x, x is a substance if and only if x is *not* limited by anything.
(2) For any x and y, if x is a substance and y limits x, then y is a substance and different from x.
(3) For any x and y, if x and y are substances and x is different from y, then x limits y and y limits x.
(4) For any x, if x is a substance, then no substance y is different from x.

Symbolizations:

1. $(x)(Sx \equiv (y)(\sim Lyx))$
2. $(x)(y)[(Sx \cdot Lyx) \supset (Sy \cdot \sim(y = x))]$

3. $\underline{\quad (x)(y)(Sy \cdot Sy \cdot \sim(x = y) \supset Lxy \cdot Ly x \quad}$
4. $(x)[Sx \supset \sim(\exists y)(Sy \cdot \sim(y = x))]$    or    $(x)[Sx \supset (y)(Sy \supset (y = x))]$

Write in the correct symbolization of 3 above.

(a) $(x)(y)[(Sx \cdot Sy \cdot \sim(x = y)) \supset (Lxy \cdot Lyx)]$

(b) $(x)(y)[(Sxy \cdot \sim(x = y)) \supset (Lxy \cdot Lyx)]$

Choice a, go to frame 190.

Choice b, go to frame 191.

# 190

Correct. The symbolization can be more easily determined if 3 is re-worded as:

> For any x and y, if x is a substance and y is a substance and x is different from y, then x limits y and y limits x.
>
> $(x)(y)[(Sx \cdot Sy \cdot \sim(x = y)) \supset (Lxy \cdot Lyx)]$

Go to page 219.

# 191

You are mistaken.

> . . . x and y are substances . . .

is a sentential function with a *multiple* subject. It should be paraphrased further to read:

> . . . x is a substance and y is a substance . . .

The *simple* predicate is

> (1) is a substance

symbolized:     S(1)

Go back to frame 189 and see how this simple predicate is used in the symbolization of 1, 2, and 4. Then choose the correct answer.

# 192

Paraphrasing the sentences on the tear out sheet, we obtain:

(1) For any x, y, and z, if z is an organized unity and x and y are distinct slices of z, then no part of x is a part of y.

Is the following a good paraphrase of 2?

For any x and y, if there is an organized unity z of which x and y are slices and x and y are distinct, then x temporally precedes y.

Yes/No

Yes. Turn to frame 193.

No. Turn to frame 194.

# 193

Statement 2 *cannot* be paraphrased as:

> For any x and y, if there is an organized unity z of which x and y are slices and x and y are distinct, then x temporally precedes y.

The antecedent of the conditional is correct but the consequent is not. We cannot say that x precedes y. What is asserted by our original sentence is that of *any* two distinct slices one of them precedes the other.

Therefore, the correct consequent reads:

> . . . then either x precedes y or y precedes x.

Turn to frame 195.

# 194

The given paraphrase does *not* do justice to the sentence.

When we say of two things x and y that *one precedes the other*, we must amplify the phrase to: *either x precedes y or y precedes x.*

You are doing well. Turn to the next frame.

(3) For any x, y, and z, if z is an organized unity and x and y are distinct slices of z, then there is a w such that w is a slice of z and w is (temporally) between x and y.

From 2 we know that if x and y are distinct slices of z, then one precedes the other. We shall not be making a material assumption, then, if we add to our *antecedent* the condition that it is x that precedes y. We now have:

(3) $(x)(y)(z)[((Oz \cdot Sxz \cdot Syz) \cdot \sim(x=y) \cdot Txy) \supset$
$(\exists w)(Swz \cdot \sim(w=x) \cdot \sim(w=y) \cdot$ w is between x and y)$]$

Using 'T' how do we symbolize: w is between x and y—illustrated below:

x　　　　　w　　　y

(time axis)

$(x)(y)(z) [((Oz \cdot Sxz \cdot Syz) \cdot \sim(x=y) \cdot Txy) \supset (\exists w)(Swz \cdot \sim(w=x) \cdot \sim(w=y) \cdot (Txw \cdot Twy))]$

---

$(Txw \cdot Twy)$　　　(We have already said: Txy)

Next frame.

# 196

Here are the paraphrases with some symbolizations:

(2) For any x and y, if there is an organized unity z such that x and y are distinct slices of z, then either x precedes y or y precedes x.

$(x)(y)[((\exists z)(Oz \cdot Sxz \cdot Syz) \cdot \sim(x=y)) \supset (Txy \lor Tyx)]$

(3) For any x, y, and z, if z is an organized unity and x and y are distinct slices of z and x precedes y, then there is a w such that w is a slice of z and w is between x and y.

$(x)(y)(z)[((Oz \cdot Sxz \cdot Syz) \cdot \sim(x=y) \cdot Txy) \supset$
$(\exists w)(Swz \cdot \sim(w=x) \cdot \sim(w=y) \cdot (Txw \cdot Twy))]$

Circle the proper symbolization of 1 below

(1) For any x, y, and z, if z is an organized unity such that x and y are distinct slices of z, then no part of x is a part of y.

A. $(x)(y)(z)[(Oz \cdot Sxz \cdot Syz \cdot \sim(x=y)) \supset \sim(w)(Pwx \supset Pwy)]$

B. $(x)(y)(z)[(Oz \cdot Sxz \cdot Syz \cdot \sim(x=y)) \supset (w)(Pwx \supset \sim Pwy)]$

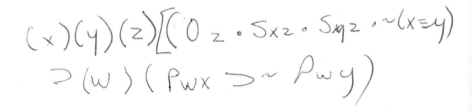

Choice A, turn to frame 197.

Choice B, turn to frame 198.

# 197

Wrong. You have been misled by ~**(w)(Pwx ⊃ Pwy)** which should be interpreted as **IT IS NOT THE CASE THAT EVERY w that is a part of x is also a part of y.** or **Not every part of x is a part of y.** which means that some parts of x *may be* parts of y.

We want to symbolize:

> *No* part of x is a part of y

or, in other words:

> Every part of x is *not* a part of y

symbolized: (w)(Pwx ⊃ ~Pwy)

Next frame.

# 198

The correct symbolization is choice B.

An analysis of Newtonian particle mechanics provides us with a problem in interpretation.

    Px: x is a particle.
    Mxy: x is the mass of y.
  Vxyzw: x is the vector force from y to z at time w.
      0: the number zero.

1. $(u)(x)(y)(z)(w)[(Px \cdot Py \cdot Vuxyz \cdot Vwyxz) \supset (u = -w)]$ (Here '$-$' is used in the mathematical sense of minus.)

    (a) For any u, x, y, z, w, if x and y are particles and u is the vector force from x to y at time z, and w is the vector force from y to x at time z, then u equals minus w.

    (b) Between any two particles at any instant of time, there are equal and oppositely directed forces.

2. $(x)(y)[(Px \cdot Myx) \supset (y > 0)]$ (Here '$>$' is used in the normal mathematical sense of 'greater than'.)

    (a) For any x and y, if x is a particle and y is the mass of x then y is greater than zero.

    (b) _A̶ Every particle has a mass_
    (Write in a reasonable English interpretation.) _more than zero_

---

The mass of any particle is greater than zero. (or: All particles have positive mass.)

Next frame.

# 199

Another problem in interpretation can be found in the theory of preference or choice:

Pxy: The subject prefers x to y

We have the following formulae:

1. $(x)(\exists y)Pyx$
2. $(x)(y)(Pxy \supset {\sim}Pyx)$
3. $(x)(y)(z)((Pxy \cdot Pyz) \supset Pxz)$

Now for 1 we have:

For any x, _there is some y the the_
_subject prefers to x._
(Complete without using *abbreviations*.)

---

For any x, there is a y such that the subject prefers y to x.

---

For 2, the interpretation is:

For any x and y, if the subject prefers x to y, then he does not prefer y to x.

And the interpretation of 3 is:

_For any x, y, & z, if the subject prefers_
_x to y, and the subject prefers y to_
_z then the subject prefers x to z._
(Again use no abbreviations.)

---

For any x, y, z, if the subject prefers x to y and y to z, then he prefers x to z.

Next frame.

# 200

(1) For any x, there is a y such that the subject prefers y to x.
(2) For any x and y, if the subject prefers x to y, then he does not prefer y to x.
(3) For any x, y, z, if the subject prefers x to y and y to z, then he prefers x to z.

Can we phrase these three into passable English?

1. Nothing is preferred above all else.

2. If one thing is preferred to another, then _the other is not prefered to the first_

---

If one thing is preferred to another, then *the other is not preferred to* the first.

---

3. If one thing is preferred to a second and the second _is_ _prefered to the third then the first is prefered to the third._

---

If one thing is preferred to a second and the second *preferred to a third, then the first is preferred to the third.*

Next frame.

# 201

Circle the correct symbolization of:
   Every senior knows at least one freshman.
      Sx: x is a senior.
      Kxy: x knows y.
      Rx: x is a freshman.

1. (x)((Sx · Kxy) ⊃ (∃y)Ry)

2. (x)(∃y)((Sx · Kxy) ⊃ Ry)

③ (x)(Sx ⊃ (∃y)(Kxy · Ry))

4. (x)(Sx ⊃ (Kxy · (∃y)Ry))


(x) Sx ⊃ (∃y) Ry • Kxy.


_____

3. (x)(Sx ⊃ (∃y)(Kxy · Ry))


If you are incorrect, go to frame 202.

If you are correct, go to frame 203.

# 202

**Every senior knows at least one freshman.** is paraphrased as:

> For any x *if* x is a senior *then* there is some (at least one) y such that (x knows y *and* y is a freshman).

From this it is an easy step to:

> (x)(Sx ⊃ (∃y)(Kxy · Ry))

Since (p · q) is logically equivalent to (q · p) we could also write:

> (x)(Sx ⊃ (∃y)(Ry · Kxy))

Next frame.

# 203

Some philosophers like no one who follows Hegel.

    Px: x is a philosopher.
    Lxy: x likes y.
    Ex: x follows Hegel.

Circle the correct symbolization of the above:

1. (∃x)(Px ·~(y)(Lxy · Ey))

2. (∃x)(Px · (y)(Ey ⊃~Lxy))

3. (∃x)(Px ⊃~(∃y)(Ey · Lxy))

4. (x)(Px ⊃ (y)~(Ey · Lxy))

$$(\exists y)(Px \cdot (y)Ey \supset \sim Lxy))$$

---

2. (∃x)(Px · (y)(Ey ⊃~Lxy))

If you are incorrect, go to frame 204.

If you are correct, go to frame 205.

# 204

**Some philosophers like no one who follows Hegel.** is paraphrased as:

> *There are some x* who are philosophers *and* who like no one who follows Hegel.

which in turn requires us to paraphrase:

> x likes no one who follows Hegel.

One reading of this is:

> For every follower of Hegel, x does not like him.

and another reading is:

> For every y, if y follows Hegel, then x does not like y.

Altogether,

> There is some x such that (x is a philosopher *and* for every y, (if y follows Hegel, then x does not like y.))

which is:     $(\exists x)(Px \cdot (y)(Ey \supset \sim Lxy))$

Next frame.

# 205

Using these abbreviations:

   Mx: x is male.

   Ex: x is female.

   Pxy: x is a parent of y.

Circle below the family relationship between k and j asserted by the following sentence. *Grandma*

$$(\exists x)(\exists y)((Pxj \cdot Pyx \cdot Pyk) \cdot Ej \cdot Mk \cdot \sim(x=k))$$

Sketching a family tree might help you.

1. j is a brother of k.

2. k is the father of j.

3. j is a grand-daughter of k.

4. k is an uncle of j.

---

4. k is an uncle of j.

If incorrect go to frame 206.

If correct go to frame 207.

# 206

$(\exists x)(\exists y)((Pxj \cdot Pyx \cdot Pyk) \cdot Ej \cdot Mk \cdot \sim(x=k))$ becomes interpreted as:

> There is an x and a y such that x is a parent of j and y is a parent of x and y is also a parent of k . . .

just this much tells us that k has a same parent as a parent of j. That is, k is a brother or sister of one of j's parents. (k is not a parent of j because of the final conjunct.)

> . . . and j is female and k is male.

The information that j is female is irrelevant to this relationship. But now we know that k is a brother of one of j's parents. Therefore, k is an uncle of j.

Next frame.

We have taken *sentential functions* and have
      (1) substituted names for variables
  or (2) quantified them
in order to construct *sentences.*

   It is also possible to construct from *sentential functions*
     (1) Names of classes
   AND (2) Names of individuals
Instead of asserting that Ludwig has the property of being a dog, we might want to say:

    1. Ludwig is a member of the class of dogs.

Using a sentential function we symbolize this as:

$$\text{l is a member of } \hat{x}Dx$$

    2. Caesar is a member of the class of noble Romans.

$$\text{c is a member of } \hat{x}(Nx \cdot Rx)$$

  How would you symbolize

    3. John is a member of the class of those who, if they play, they study hard.
       j: John
     Px: x plays
     Sx: x studies hard

*j is a member of $\hat{x}(Px \supset Sx)$*

---

3. j is a member of $\hat{x}(Px \supset Sx)$

Next frame.

# 208

We can assert that two is less than three by our usual method:

L23 or 2 < 3

or we can use the notation of classes:

(a) The pair (2,3) is a member of the class of *ordered* pairs such that the first is less than the second.

(b) (2,3) is a member of $\hat{x}\hat{y}(x < y)$

Notice also that we could say that

(a) 2 is a member of the class of things less than 3.

(b) 2 is a member of $\hat{x}(x < 3)$

If we abbreviate 'is a member of' in the usual way by '$\epsilon$' we can symbolize:

All members of the class of Greeks are members of the class of mortal things.

as: $(y)(y\epsilon\hat{x}Rx \supset y\epsilon\hat{x}Mx)$

How should we symbolize:

The class of beautiful mermaids has no members.
Bx: x is beautiful.
Mx: x is a mermaid.

$\sim(\exists y)(y\epsilon \, \hat{x}(Bx \cdot Mx)$

*watch brackets*

---

$\sim(\exists y)(y\epsilon\hat{x}(Bx \cdot Mx))$     or     $\sim(\exists y)(y\epsilon\hat{x}Bx \cdot y\epsilon\hat{x}Mx)$

Next frame.

# 209

We write **k is a member of the class of those x such that Bx** as:

$k \epsilon \hat{x} Bx$

Some authors *abstract* the name of a class from a sentential function using slightly different notation. For them

$\hat{x} Bx$      is symbolized:      $\{x | Bx\}$

Thus they would write:      $k \epsilon \{x | Bx\}$      for **k is a member of the class of x such that Bx.**

What is the meaning of:      $\sim(k \epsilon \hat{x} Bx)$      (sometimes written: $k \notin \hat{x} Bx$)?

*K is not a member of the class such that By*

---

k is not a member of the class of those x such that Bx.

Next frame.

# 210

Fx is a sentential function.

(∃x)Fx and (x)Fx are sentences, and are either True or False.

x̂Fx (or: {x|Fx}) is a *name* of a class, and is neither True nor False.

To say that something is a member of a class is to assert a sentence and thus to assert what is True or False.

(∃y)(y∈x̂Fx) is either True or False. It is also logically equivalent to

(∃y)Fy (and: (∃x)Fx).

~(y)(y∈x̂Fx) is logically equivalent to three of the following sentences. Circle the one it is *not* equivalent to.

1. ~(y)Fy

2. (y)(y∉x̂Fx)

3. (∃y)(y∉x̂Fx)

4. ~(x)(x∈x̂Fx)

---

2. (y)(y∉x̂Fx)     This asserts that nothing is a member of the class denoted by x̂Fx.

Next frame.

# 211

There are various assertions involving classes that one can make:

A certain individual, say k, is a member of the class: $k\epsilon\{x|Fx\}$

Something is a member of the class: $(\exists y)(y\epsilon\hat{x}Fx)$

One can also say that one class is a member of another class:

$\hat{x}Fx\epsilon\hat{y}Gy$

or, that one class is a *subclass* of another class: $\hat{y}Gy \subset \dot{z}Hz$

or, even that one class is *identical* to another: $\hat{x}Rx = \hat{y}Sy$

Put the correct sign between the names of the above two classes.

---

The identity sign, =, therefore, $\hat{x}Rx = \hat{y}Sy$

Next frame.

240